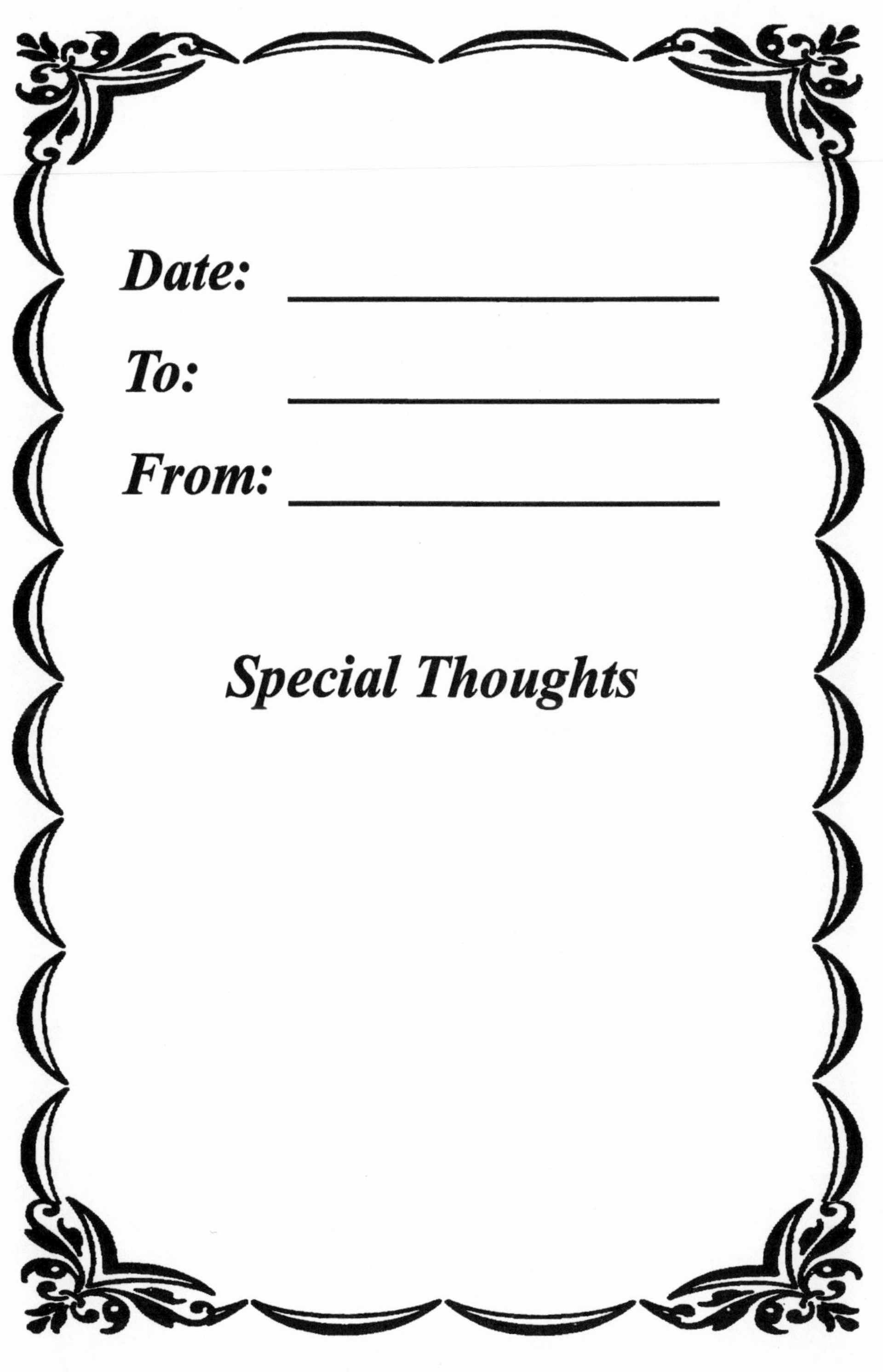

Date: ______________________

To: ______________________

From: ______________________

Special Thoughts

A Journal to Live By

by

John J. Pelizza, Ph.D.
Joseph G. Pelizza, P.T.

Published by:
Pelizza & Associates
PO Box 225
North Chatham, NY 12132

Photograph, Cover & Text Design by: Bonnie S. Pelizza

Published by Pelizza & Associates, PO Box 225, North Chatham, New York 12132, (518) 766-4849.

http://www.pelizza.com

Printed and bound in the United States of America.
ISBN 0-9614872-5-9

Dedication and Acknowledgement

Dedication

This book is dedicated to Bonnie, beloved wife and mother, who inspired many of the ideas in this book and kept us on track. Your support, encouragement, patience, and most importantly love, will always be valued and cherished. We thank you.

Acknowledgement

We would like to extend a "special" thank you to Julie A. Testo for taking our ideas and transforming them into poems that touch the heart.

Table of Contents

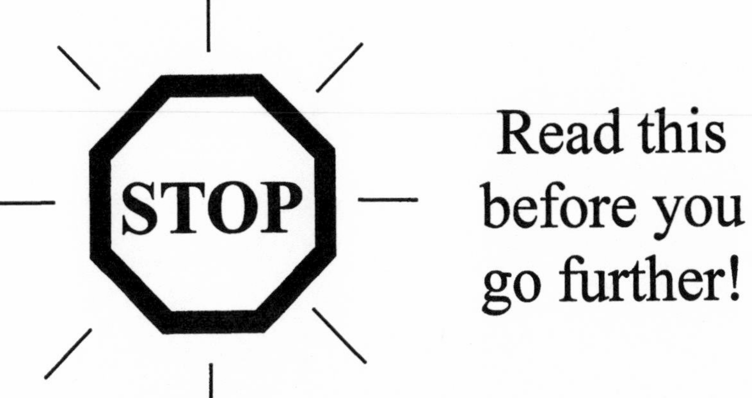

This is a Take Action Journal. Yes, it is important to put your thoughts, ideas, concerns, and problems on paper. But in the end, you must take action to make a situation better.

The action could be to think differently, or the action may be to physically do something. **Action is the antidote to pessimism (inertia). It's the ultimate energizer.**

When you write in your journal, keep asking yourself what actions, either mental or physical, will make things better. Thinking and acting this way will create wonderful things in your life . . .

You become Optimistic, Hopeful,
Excited and have Direction.

The Journey . . .

Life

is a journey . . .

and

you're somewhere . . .

on that road!

INTRODUCTION

Taking Action to Gain Control

A journal is a place to initiate change in your life. Journaling will help you to discover yourself and motivate you to take risks, to change and make positive breakthroughs. The goal of this journal is to get you to think better, feel better and act better. It is a life-long process.

Journal writing will give you courage to pursue your goals, and that courage will come from within you. **This journal is YOURS.** The goal of journal writing is to get your thoughts and feelings on paper. Acting on those thoughts and feelings is the essential step. Then work your journal so it works best for you. When writing, do not think about grammar, spelling or punctuation. Your focus in writing will be expression that leads to action. Your focus should not be perfection. Writing will become the private place to express what matters to you, the significant parts of your life; these usually include love and pain. You need to be honest in your writing. The honesty in journal writing will help you decide exactly what you want in life. This will help you understand your past, so you can enjoy the present and create a better future.

Make your journal personal to you; draw pictures and create graphs if that helps make your journal come alive. Make journaling a vehicle to express all of your inner thoughts, feelings and goals. Your decision to start is the first action that will get you there. **We guarantee that your journal writing will help you think, feel and act more positively in all aspects of your life.** We can assure you that your willingness to keep an active journal of your life will energize you. The more you journal write and **take action** the better you will feel.

Journal writing begins always with thinking. Journal writing produces the kind of thinking that gets a person focused on his/her life. When you write in your journal, you will better understand your thoughts, feelings and actions. These thoughts will guide you to take action. The central theme in your thoughts will be reflection on your life: Is your life good? Is it bad? Is it in the middle? When thinking about your life, think about what is both emotional and personal. This process will begin to create hope in your life.

The feelings produced in journal writing will lead you

to positive action. Making your entries will help you relax in order to find perspective and make a "plan of action." Your feelings will get you in touch with yourself as well as cause you to initiate action that will help you achieve your goals. When you can feel that place you want to be, as your pen writes, you will discover the necessary actions that will take you there and make you better.

The first time you write in your journal, you start taking action. As soon as you decide to do it, you are acting and building energy. By creating the physical form in writing, you can reflect on past and future actions. When you write in your journal, you will be collecting and analyzing past and current data about yourself. Honest analysis of this data will inspire you to make the necessary changes to improve your quality of life. By studying your behavior, you will see that action matters. Journal writing will lead you to see that **KNOWLEDGE + ACTION = BIG BENEFITS.** Knowledge of personal behavior is the ultimate benefit of journal writing; it gets us to take more action to improve our lives. Journal writing shows us that action improves the overall quality of life. Journal writing is the physical form that a person can look back at, read again, and be energized by when that person has achieved the plan of action.

Energy comes from whatever you achieve. Energy

comes from the process of creating new thoughts and new structures. As you write more, you will produce more energy to think, feel and act better.

The energy in journal writing helps us work better, live better, and do better. It creates balance in our lives and can reduce stress and anxiety.

Studies show that people who express their deepest thoughts and feelings in a journal can improve their health by increasing t-cell production, which helps keep immunity strong. When you write, you are putting your thoughts and feelings in a physical form, and that's therapeutic. In addition to the emotional and physical benefits of journal writing, such as high energy and good health, journal writing produces a significant historical artifact, the **"legacy of your life."**

The greatest benefit in journal writing is positive self-expectancy. When you start journal writing, you can expect that you will get better. The human condition does not stand still. You are either getting better, or you are getting worse. If you want to do better, you have to change something.

Get out your pen!

Start writing by answering this question.

What do You Value?

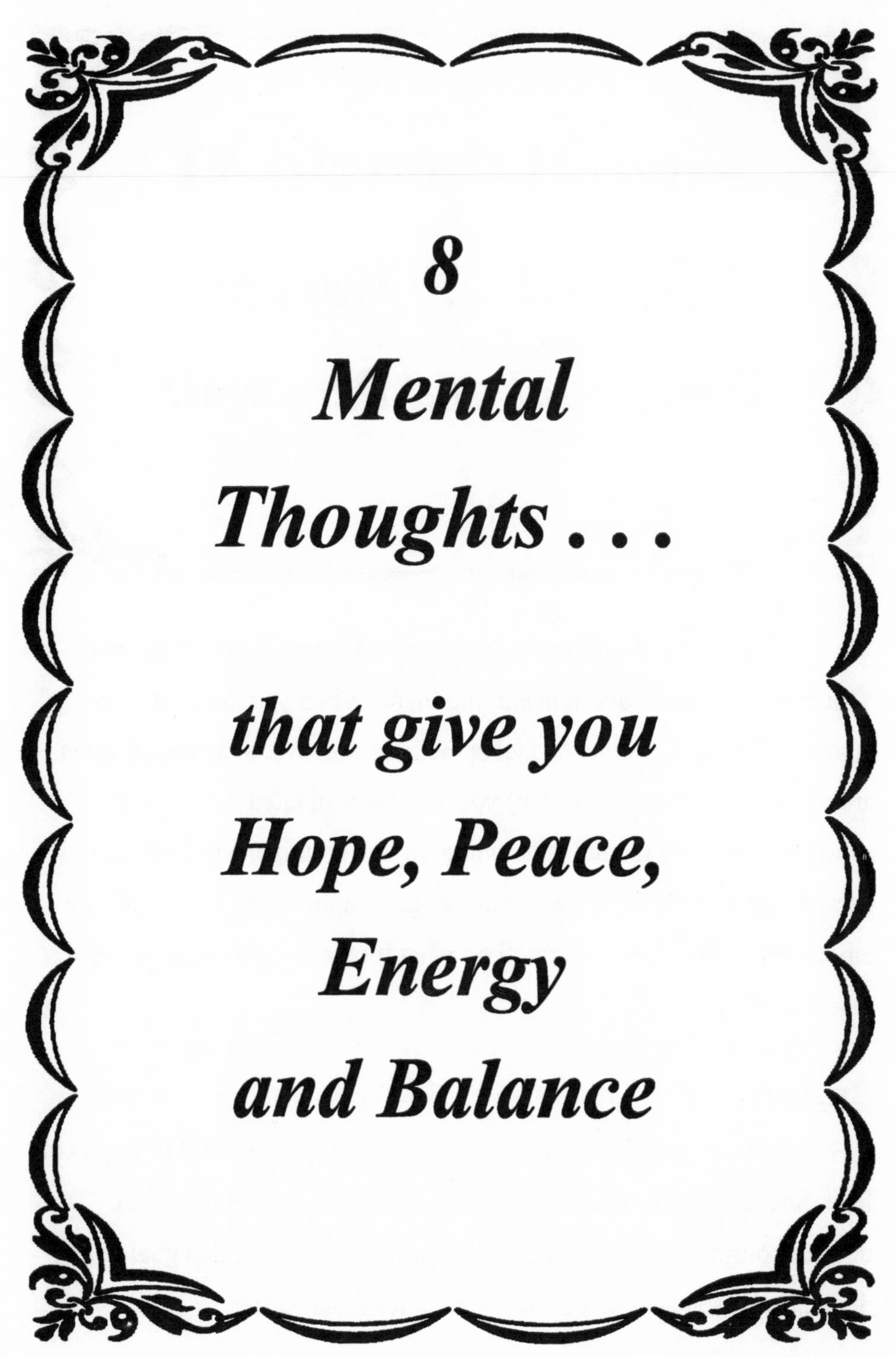

8

Mental Thoughts . . .

that give you Hope, Peace, Energy and Balance

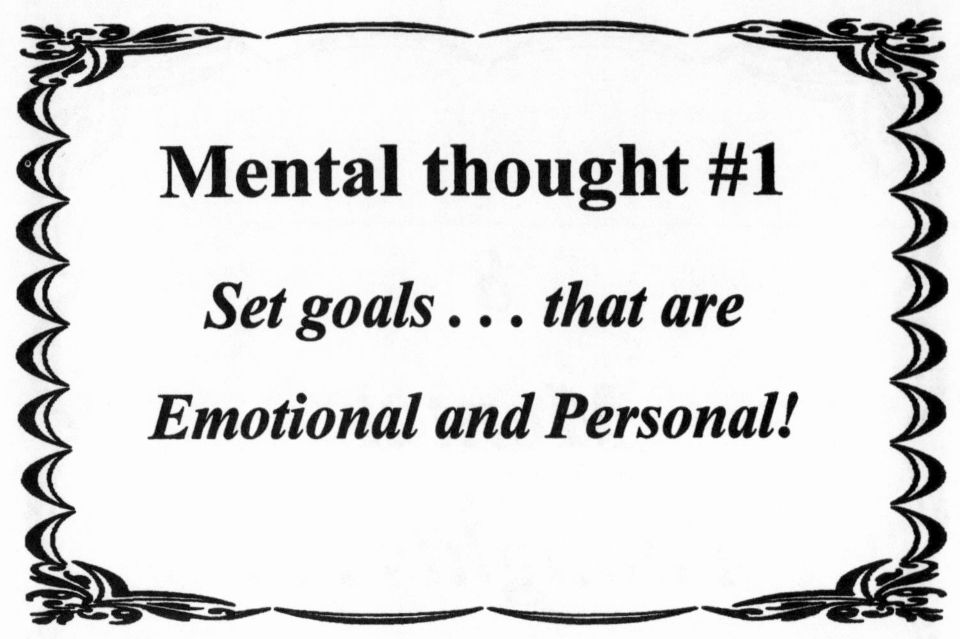

Mental thought #1

Set goals . . . that are Emotional and Personal!

Your goals should get you excited when you think about them. You must really care about achieving them. When you think of your goals, they should get you to feel something positive. When your goals are emotional and personal (EP) you will be motivated to plan and achieve them. This mental state will give you courage, confidence, and persistence to continue on when things get tough. When your goals are emotional and personal, you will do what it takes to achieve them, and that's exciting.

Example:

Take the single mother whose goal is to put her child through college. She deals with taking another job to help pay for college and doesn't complain about being tired or burned out. Since this goal is EP, dealing with setbacks or obstacles becomes much easier.

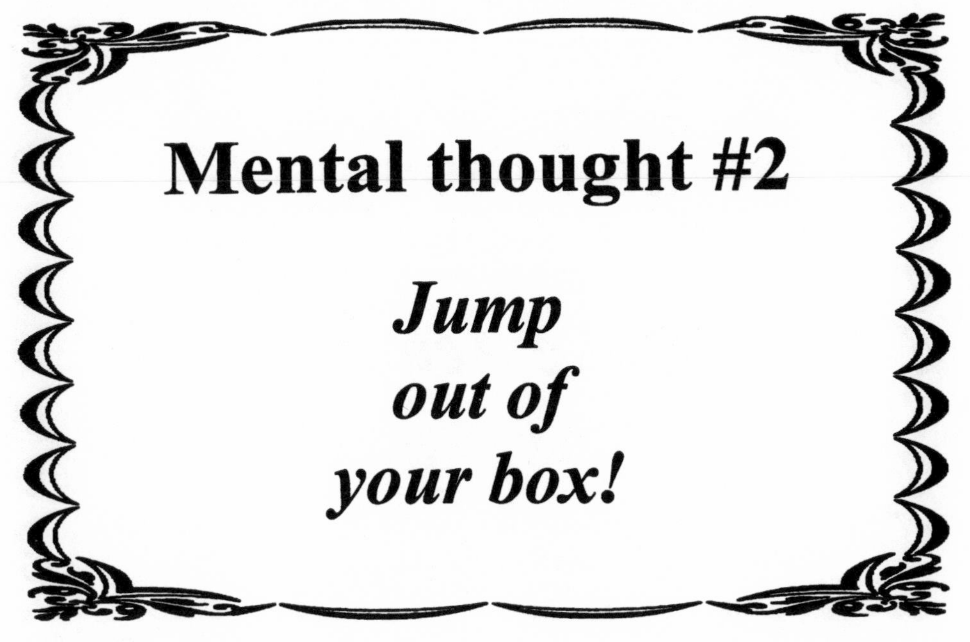

Mental thought #2

Jump out of your box!

Be willing to do new things. Take risks. When you risk with negative expectations, you will deplete your energy levels. When you risk with positive expectations, you will create high levels of energy. The secret is your expectation of the risk. Risking will bring you to places that you have never been to before, both physically and mentally. Believe us, it's fun. Do it!

Example:

Start small; eat at different restaurants, see movies you are not accustomed to, or begin a new exercise routine. Next, work up to bigger risks, like going on a roller coaster ride, asking for a raise at work, applying for a new job, buying a new home, or moving to another state.

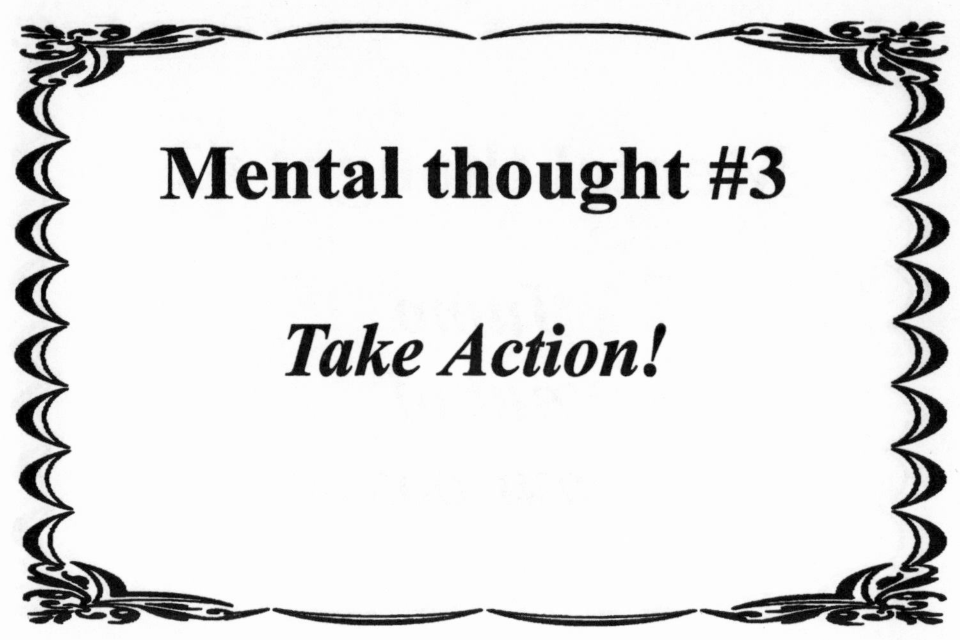

Mental thought #3

Take Action!

Nothing happens unless we take an action. As soon as you take an action, your body creates energy. And you feel better! Deciding, writing, and doing are all actions. All three will energize you. The more actions you take, the better you will feel, and the more you accomplish, the more hopeful you will become. Continue the action process throughout your life, and you'll experience and achieve your dreams. That's invigorating!

Example:

Let's say a goal of yours is to take a cruise. First shot of energy will come from deciding to go on the cruise. Second shot of energy will come from writing about the decision in your journal. Third shot of energy will come from actually booking the cruise. Fourth shot of energy will come from enjoying the cruise. Fifth shot of energy will come from the memories that will be with you for the rest of your life.

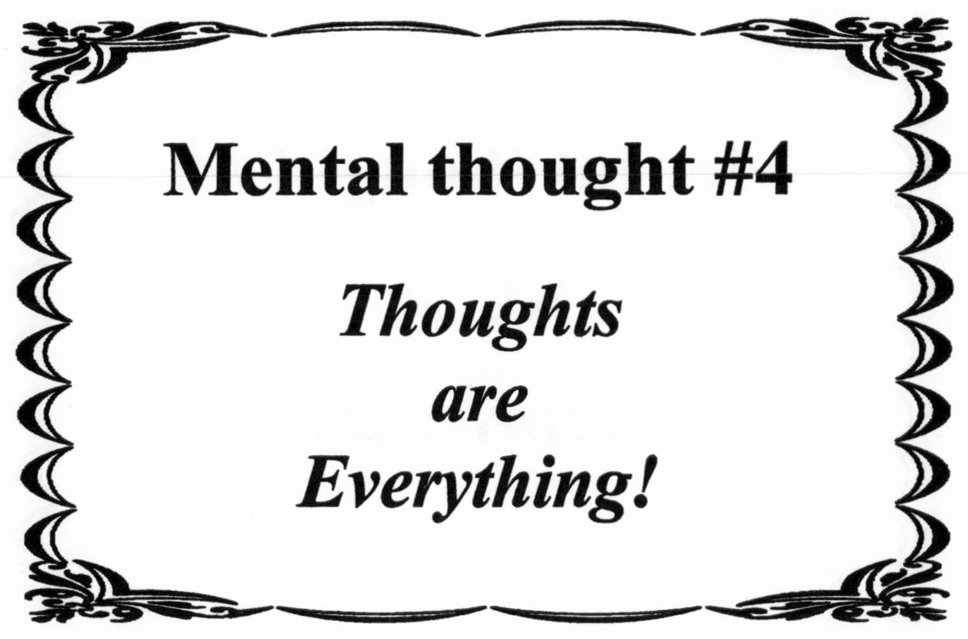

Mental thought #4

Thoughts are Everything!

What you think about makes you feel the way you feel. How you feel influences what you do and what you don't do. It's important that you choose optimistic thoughts that energize you moment by moment. Choosing to think this way will help you take more positive actions to reach your goals. This will create harmony and balance in your life.

<u>Example:</u>

Your loved one came home late for dinner. The food is cold. You could be very upset he/she is late, or you could be thankful your loved one made it home safely. This is the same situation with just different thoughts creating opposite energy levels. Remember, your thoughts create your energy levels.

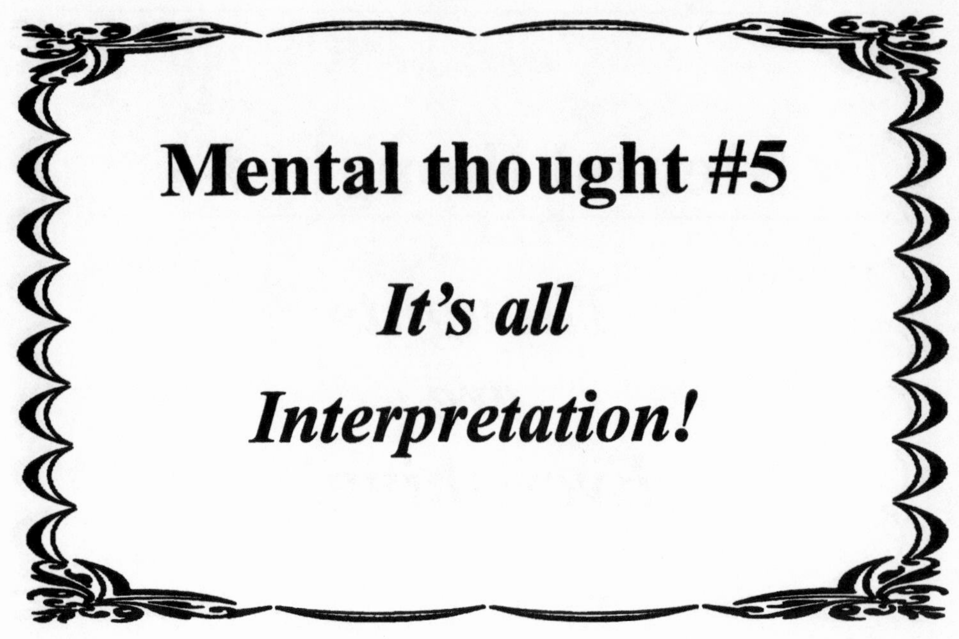

Mental thought #5

It's all Interpretation!

You can't always control the events in your life, but you can control how you interpret them. How you interpret them will cause you to feel a certain way, which will influence what decisions and actions you choose to take. When you experience a negative event in your life, you need to ask yourself three questions, which will help move you through the experience.

The Three Questions:

1. Can I die from it? Probably not.
2. How can I learn and grow from it? Find it and do it. There are many ways.
3. What can I do to make the situation better? Just do it.

Example:

Car doesn't start for work.

1. Will you die from it?

   No.

2. How can you learn and grow?

   Tune your car up more often, have a backup ride for work.

3. How can you make it better?

   Call a friend, co-worker, or a taxi to get you to work.

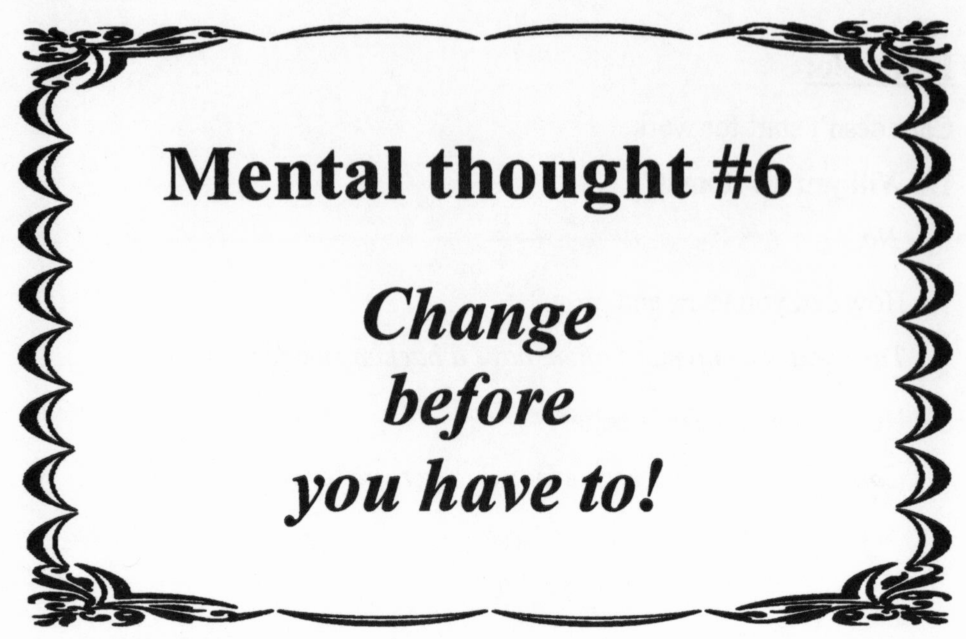

Mental thought #6

Change before you have to!

Change is good. It's the only way to do better. When you change before you have to, you get a better deal. When forced to change because of power and authority, usually there is more pain and less good. Remember, **change is only a moment in time.** The change process is broken down into one moment when you are thinking and behaving one way and the next moment you are not. This is terrific news. It means we have the power to change our thoughts, feelings, and actions at any moment in time. Like right now!

Example:

On September 11, 2001, one moment you were thinking and behaving one way, and the next moment you were thinking and behaving differently.

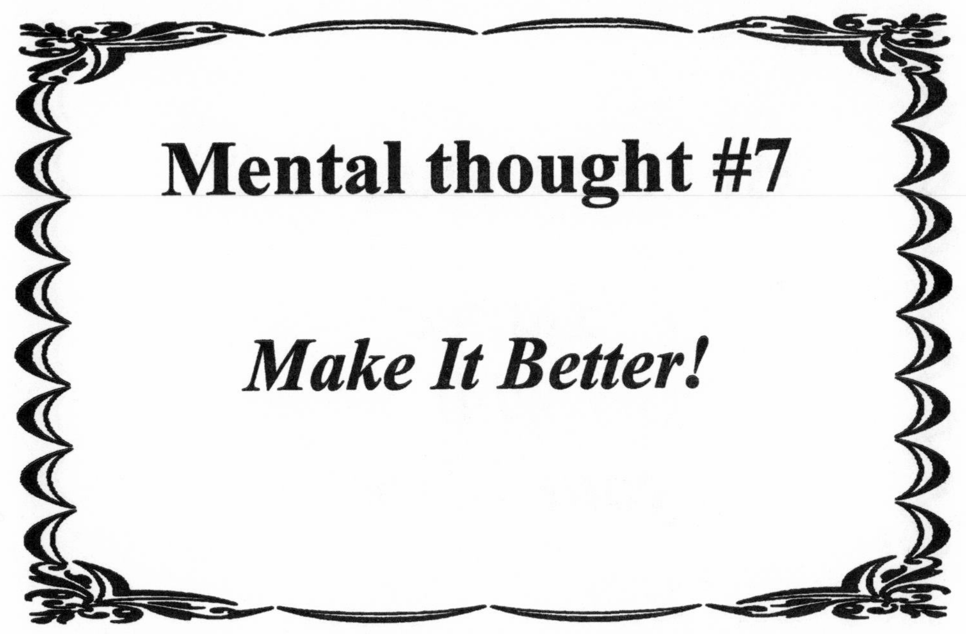

Mental thought #7

Make It Better!

We can always make a situation better. There are times when a situation is so bad that you may not be able to make it good. However, with positive actions you can always make the situation better. You must also recognize that there will be times when you are taking positive actions, feeling better, and yet a level of good still hasn't been reached. That's ok. As long as you continue to take action, you will reach your destination or be very close. Now that is exciting!

Example:

Your best friend Bob has a death in his family. Bob is grieving and not feeling well. You bring soup, salad and bread over to his home. Even though Bob is not back to feeling good, he is probably feeling better. Your act of kindness has made a difficult situation better.

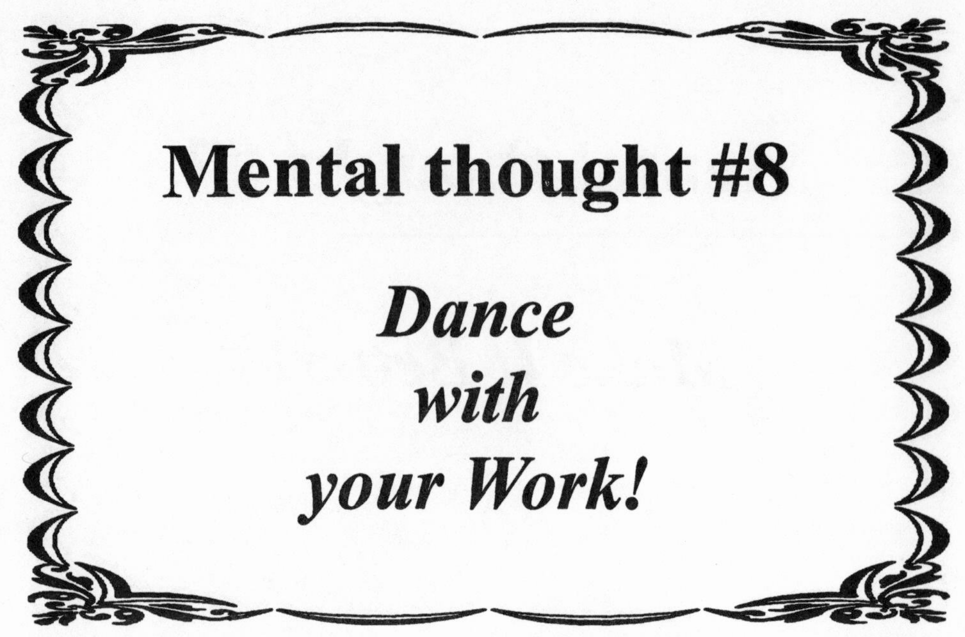

Mental thought #8

Dance with your Work!

When you work hard, you have an opportunity to produce, invent, create, contribute, and serve. All of these will produce energy in your body. Work provides for your family and loved ones. Doing excellent work energizes you.

The process of working hard allows you the opportunity to develop your skills and talents to the highest level. People who become excellent in their work do well. It is important to value your work. You should recognize that your work can lead you to what you value in life. When you can't find value in your work, you should find other work.

The paradox of work is this: When you love your work, it is no longer considered work. Wouldn't it be wonderful if you valued your work and it provided for you and your family? When this happens, you have a fantastic situation. It is really out there. All you need to do is find it. It is worth searching for.

Example:

Assembly workers may not like the specific tasks they are required to do. If, however, the pay and fringe benefits provide these people with what they value for their family, then they are happy with their work.

High school coaches get paid very little per hour for their services. However, because they value and love coaching, they enjoy their work.

4 Steps on How to Use Your Journal

Step 1:

Question: How often should I write in my journal?

Answer: Whatever feels appropriate. We recommend a minimum of once a week or as often as you like. Length of each entry can vary from one sentence to several pages. The more consistent you are in your journal entries, the better you will do.

Step 2:

Question: How do I use the 8 Mental Thoughts?

Answer: The 8 Mental Thoughts are designed to help you think and take action. When writing, ask yourself, "Am I applying the Mental Thoughts?" The more you apply the mental thoughts, the better you will do.

Step 3:

Question: How do I use the Quotes?

Answer: Throughout the 87 Quotes, there are 8 questions. When you see a question, think about it, answer it (write it down), ACT ON IT! The remaining quotes are designed to help you think about what's important in your life. READ each quote and jot down ideas around the quote on how it can influence your life.

Step 4:

Question: How do I use My Accomplishments, pages 214-216?

Answer: Throughout your journal writing you will be writing down things you would like to accomplish. Pages 214-216 are designed for you to list your accomplishments as you achieve them.

Let the Journey begin . . .

What do YOU want
out of life?

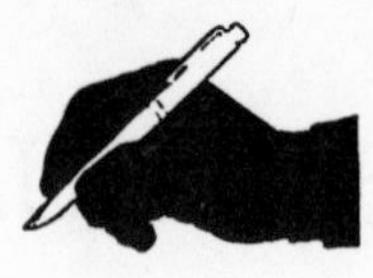

YOU are
your best resource!

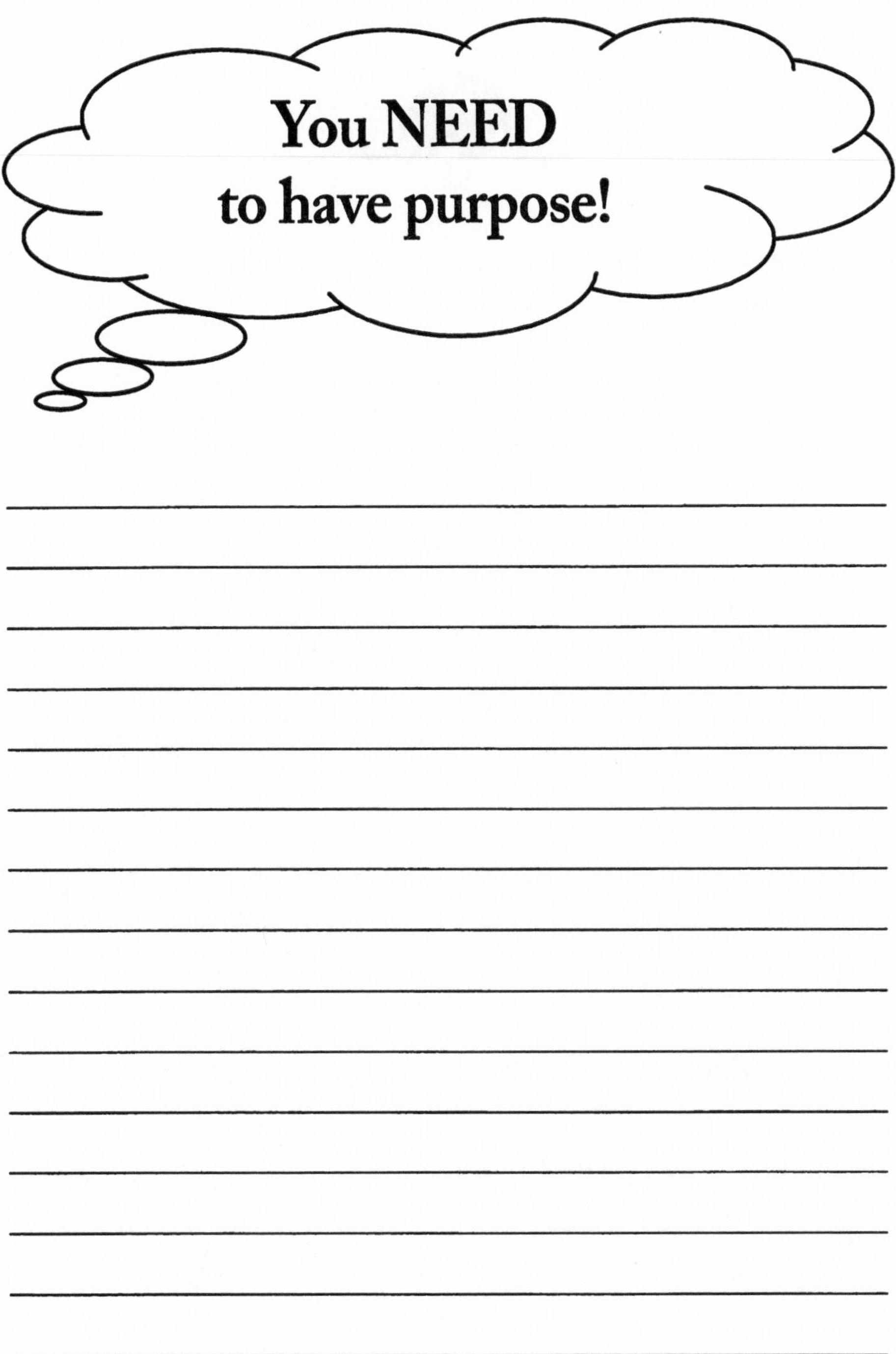
You NEED
to have purpose!

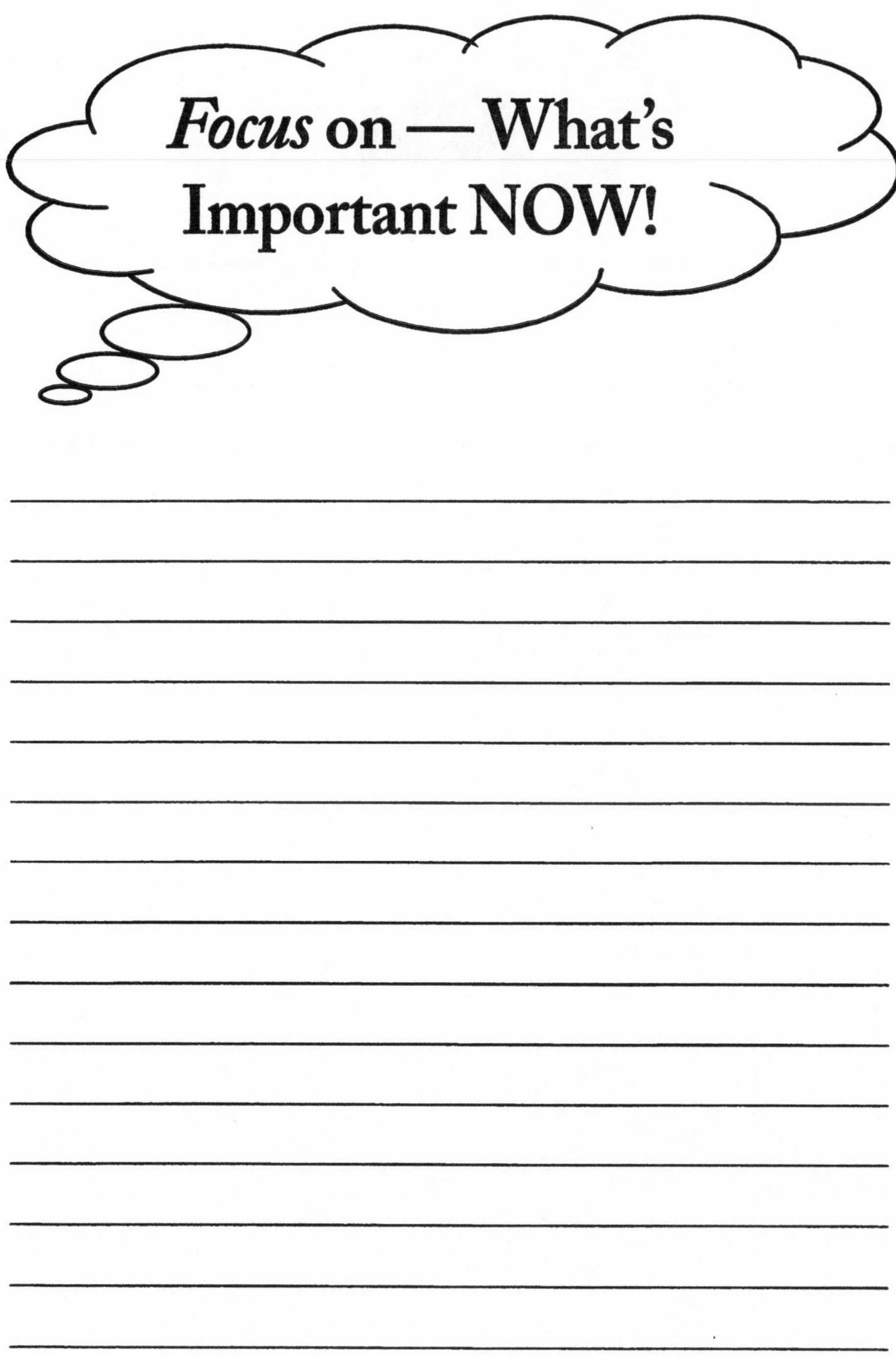
Focus on — What's
Important NOW!

To learn more about this quote - refer to page 14

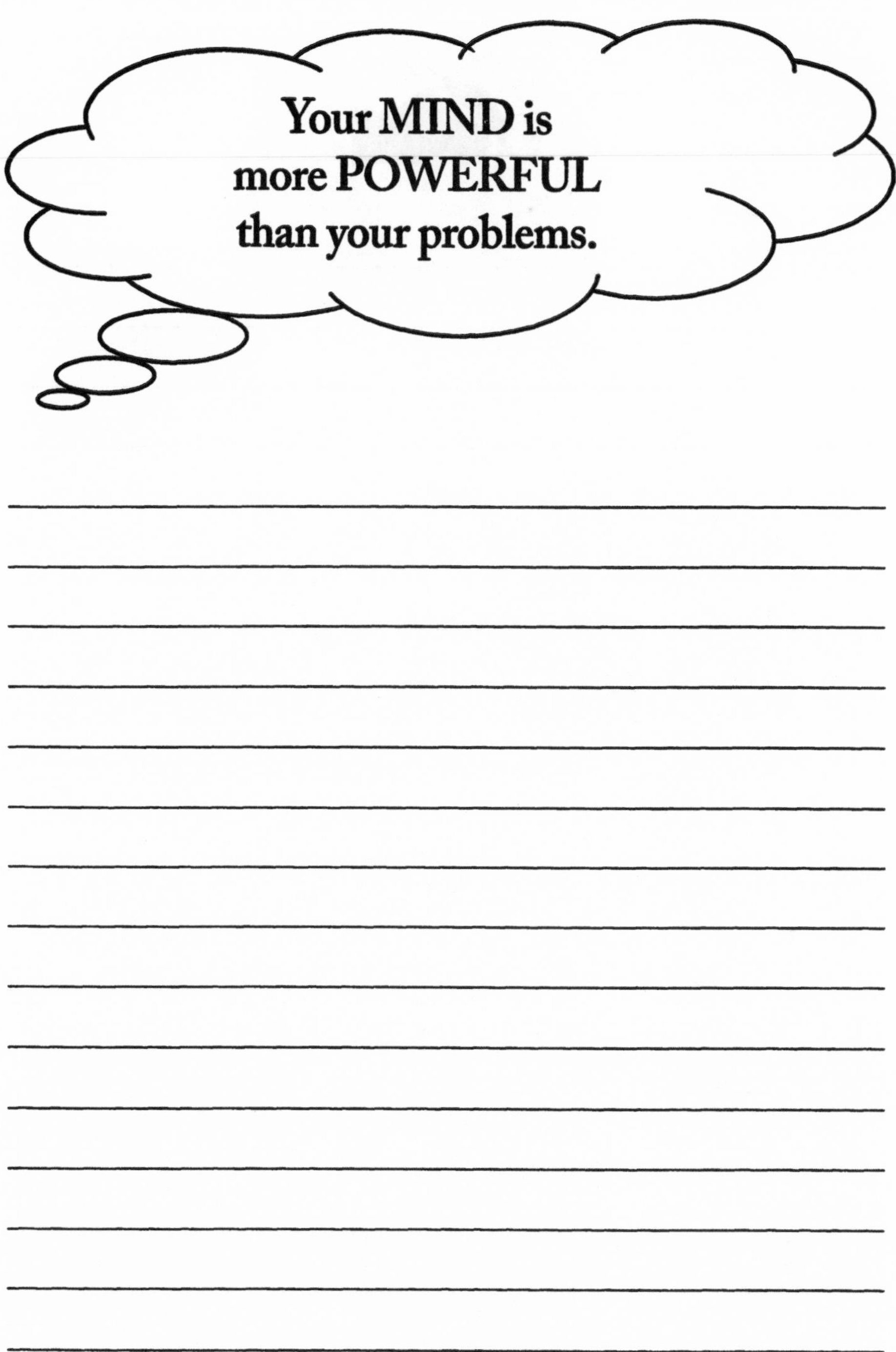
Your MIND is
more POWERFUL
than your problems.

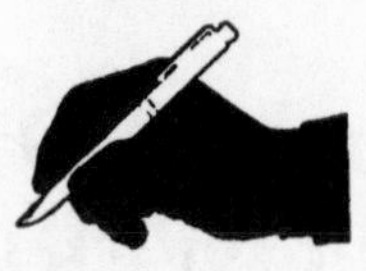

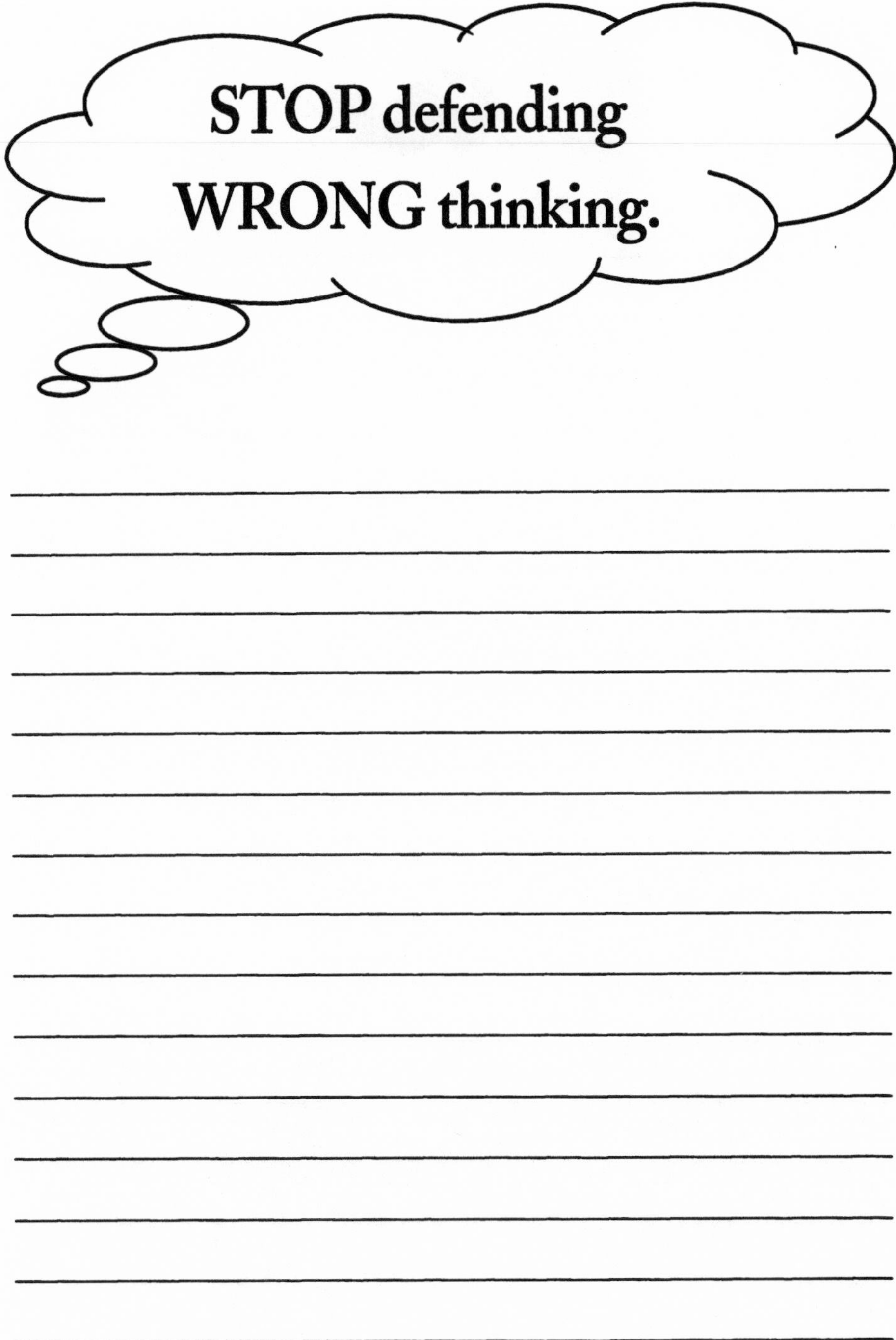
STOP defending
WRONG thinking.

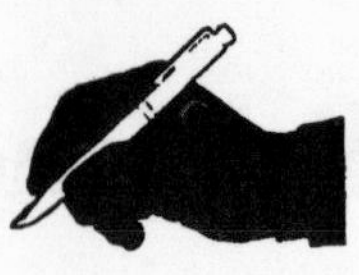

Are you on the
RIGHT path?

To learn more about this quote - refer to page 12

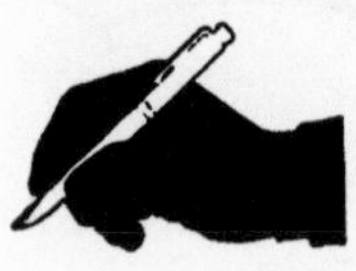

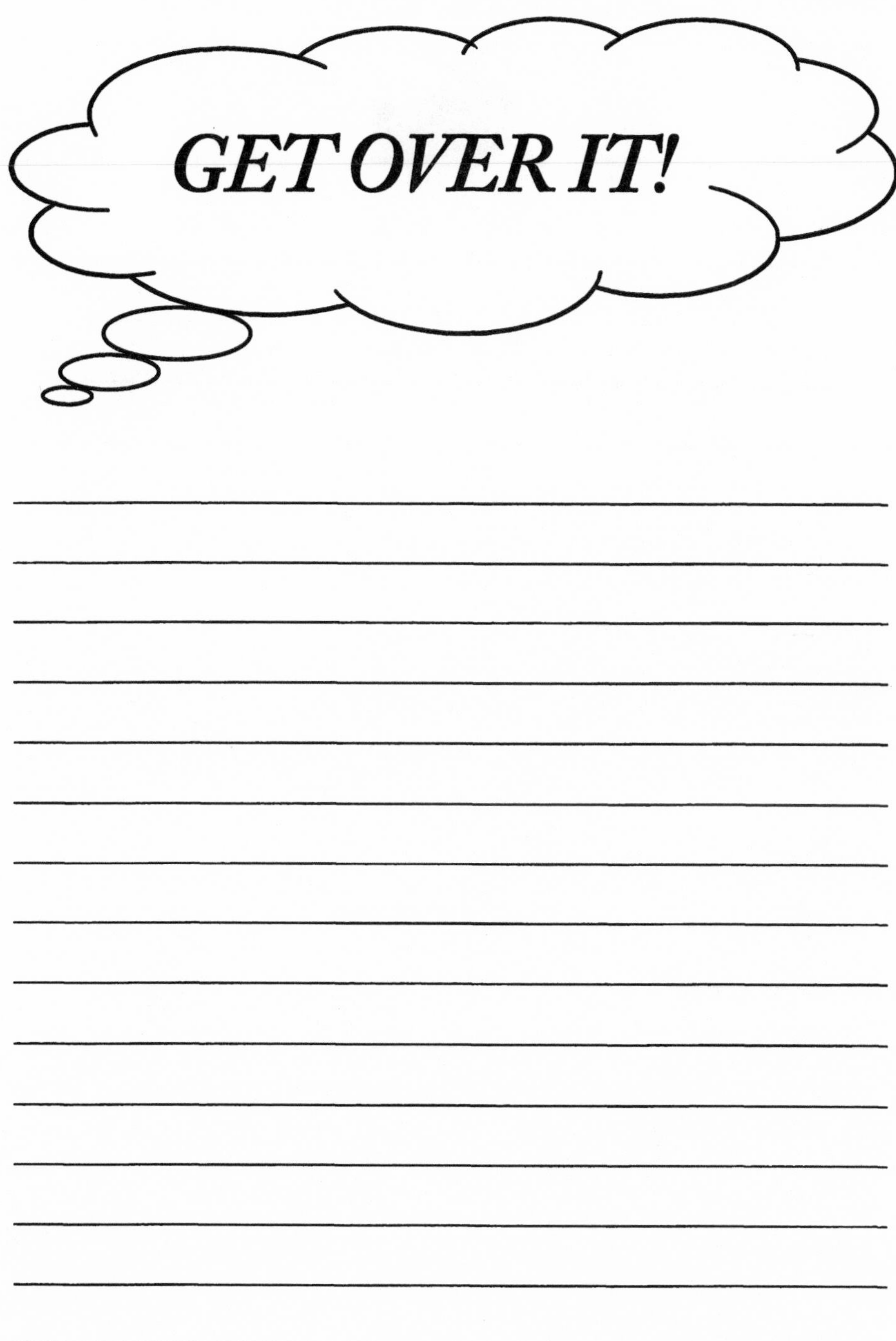
GET OVER IT!

The Birth of a Child...

Is not the birth of a season
Is not the birth of a simple reason
To make sense of today and yesterday
While little thoughts float away.

The Birth of a Child . . .
Is not just part of it.
Is not just the start of it.
Is not just the heart of it.
The birth of a child is all.
The birth of a child is all.

The Birth of a child . . .
Is not a little sign
Nor a little person to call mine.

The Birth of a child . . .
Is all.
The Birth a child . . .
Will call.

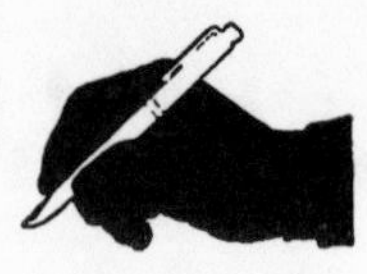

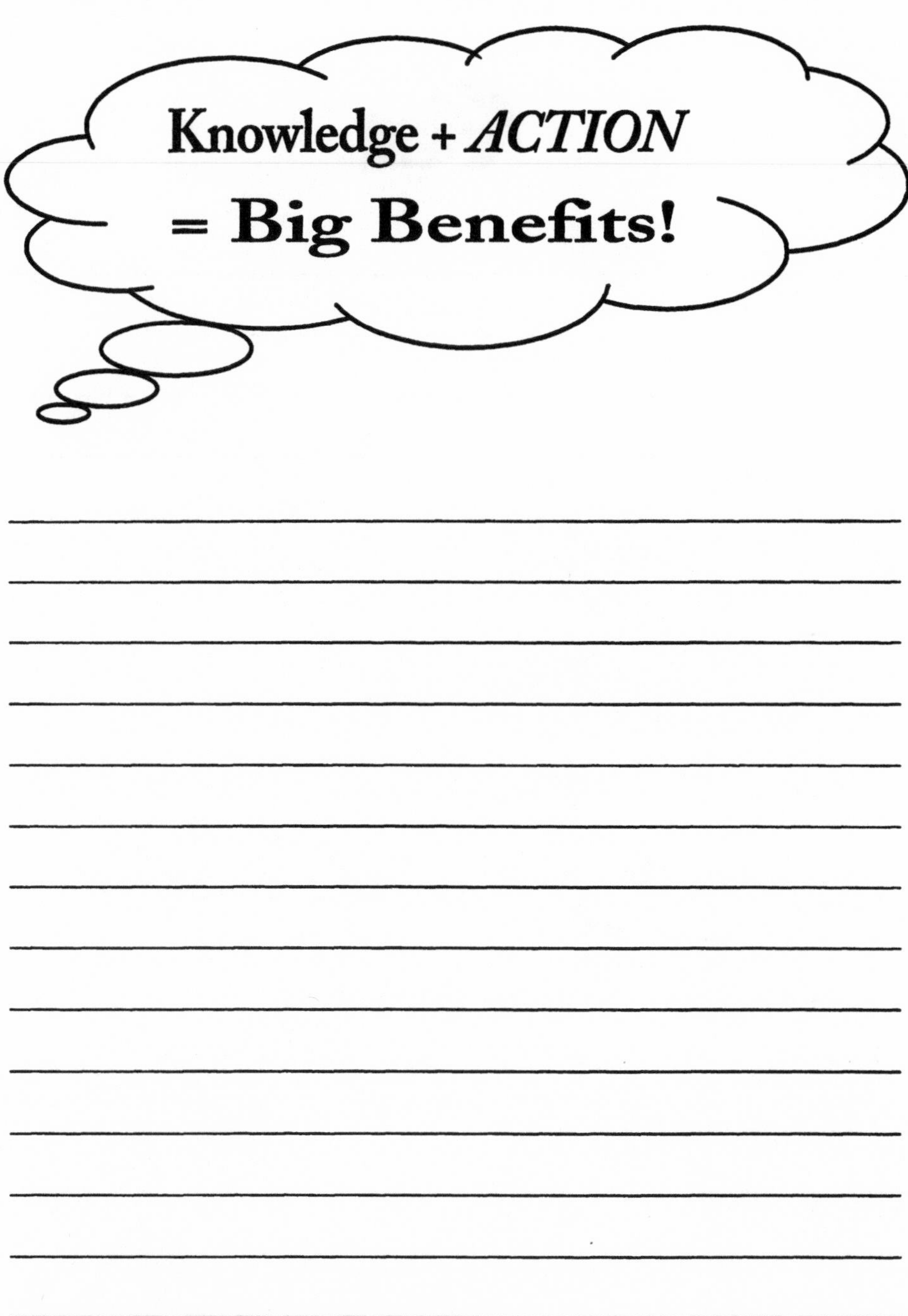
Knowledge + *ACTION*
= Big Benefits!

To learn more about this quote - refer to page 14

DECIDE!!!

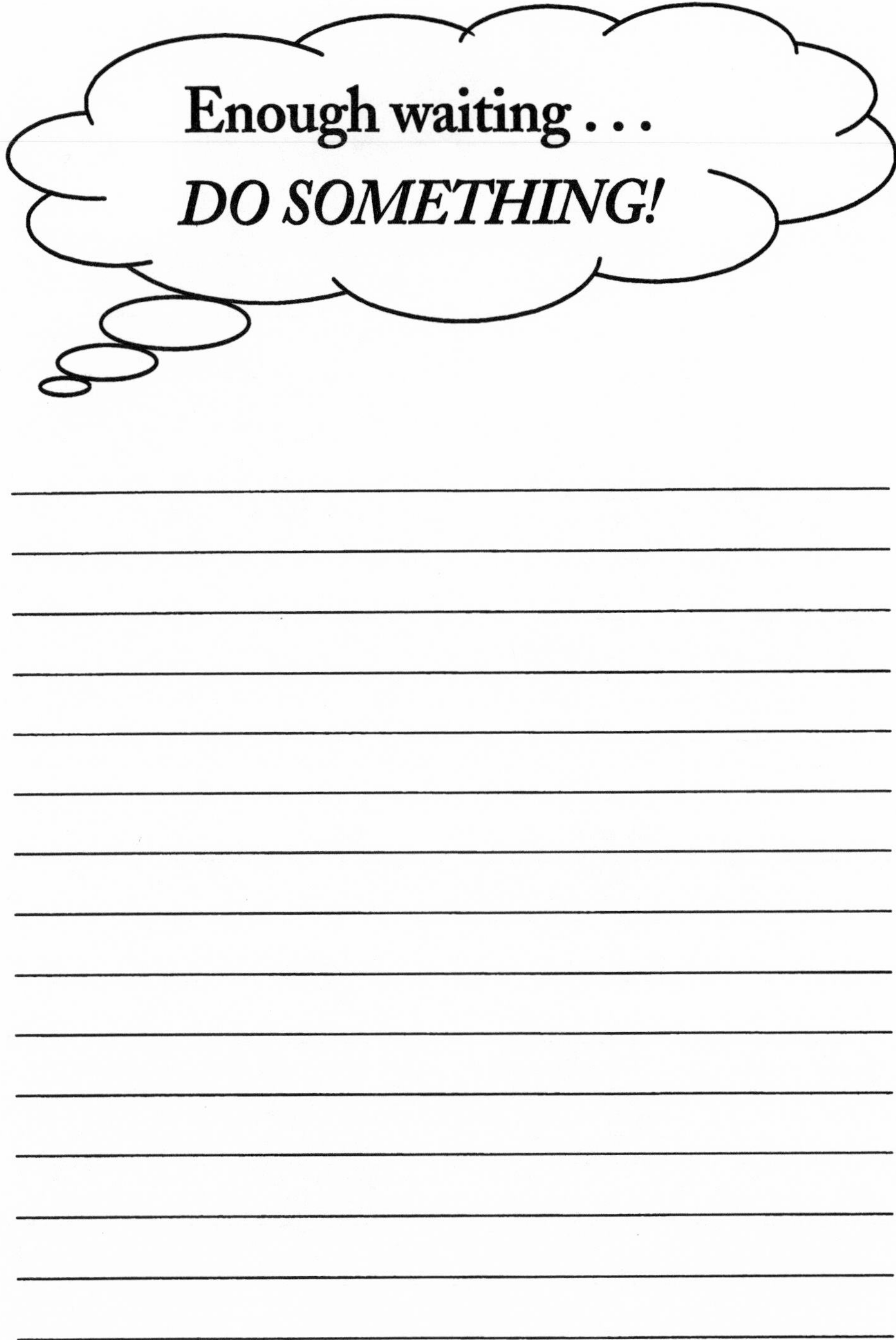
Enough waiting . . .
DO SOMETHING!

Stop Whinnnnnning!

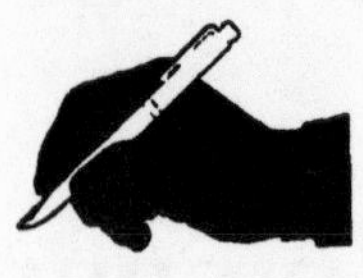

Are you a PRETENDER
or a
CONTENDER?

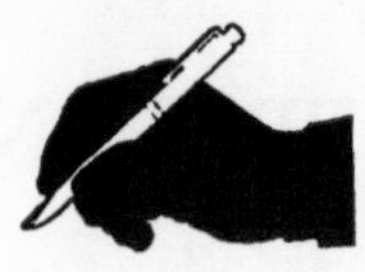

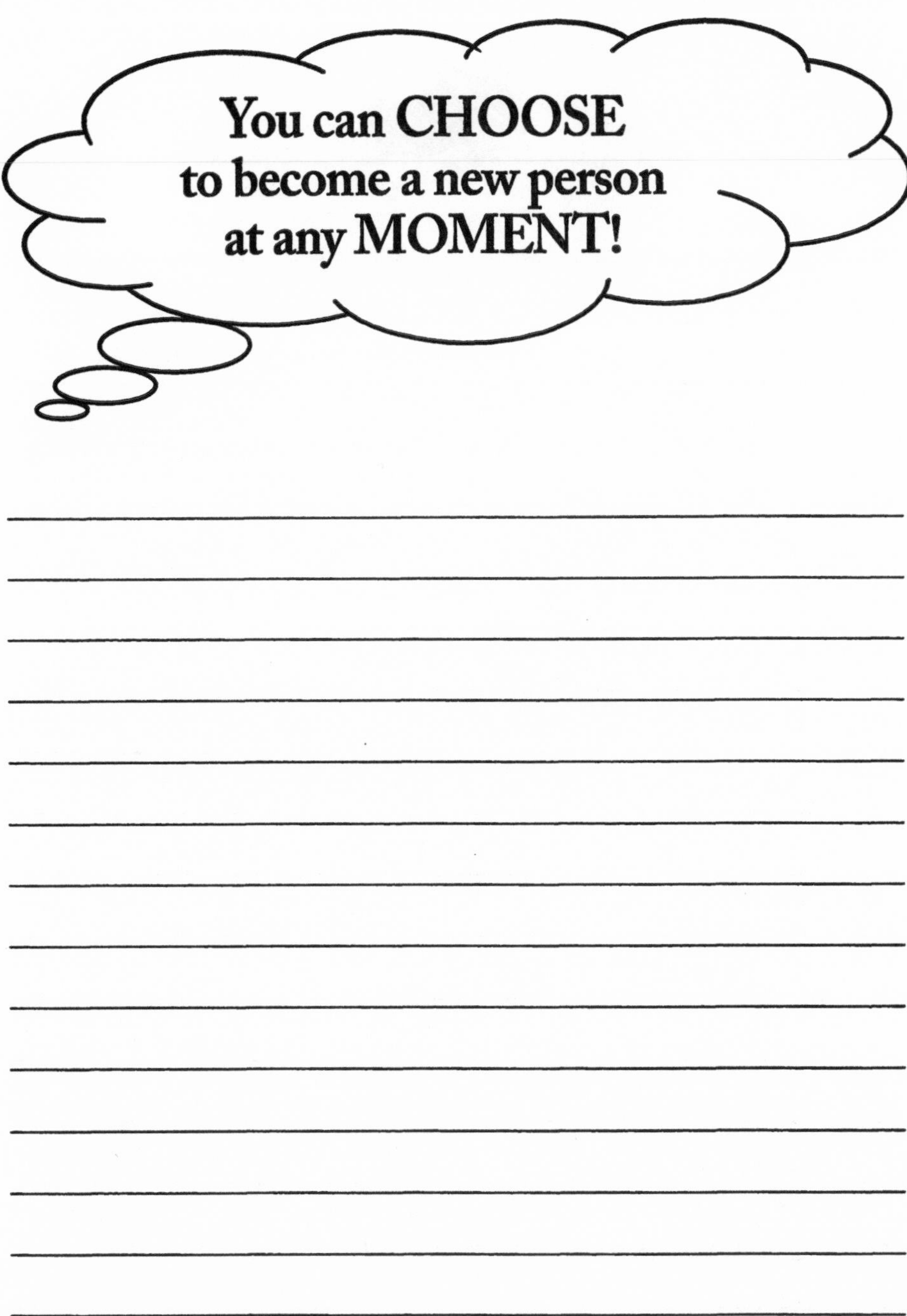
You can CHOOSE
to become a new person
at any MOMENT!

To learn more about this quote - refer to page 18

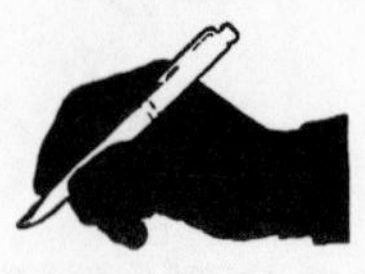

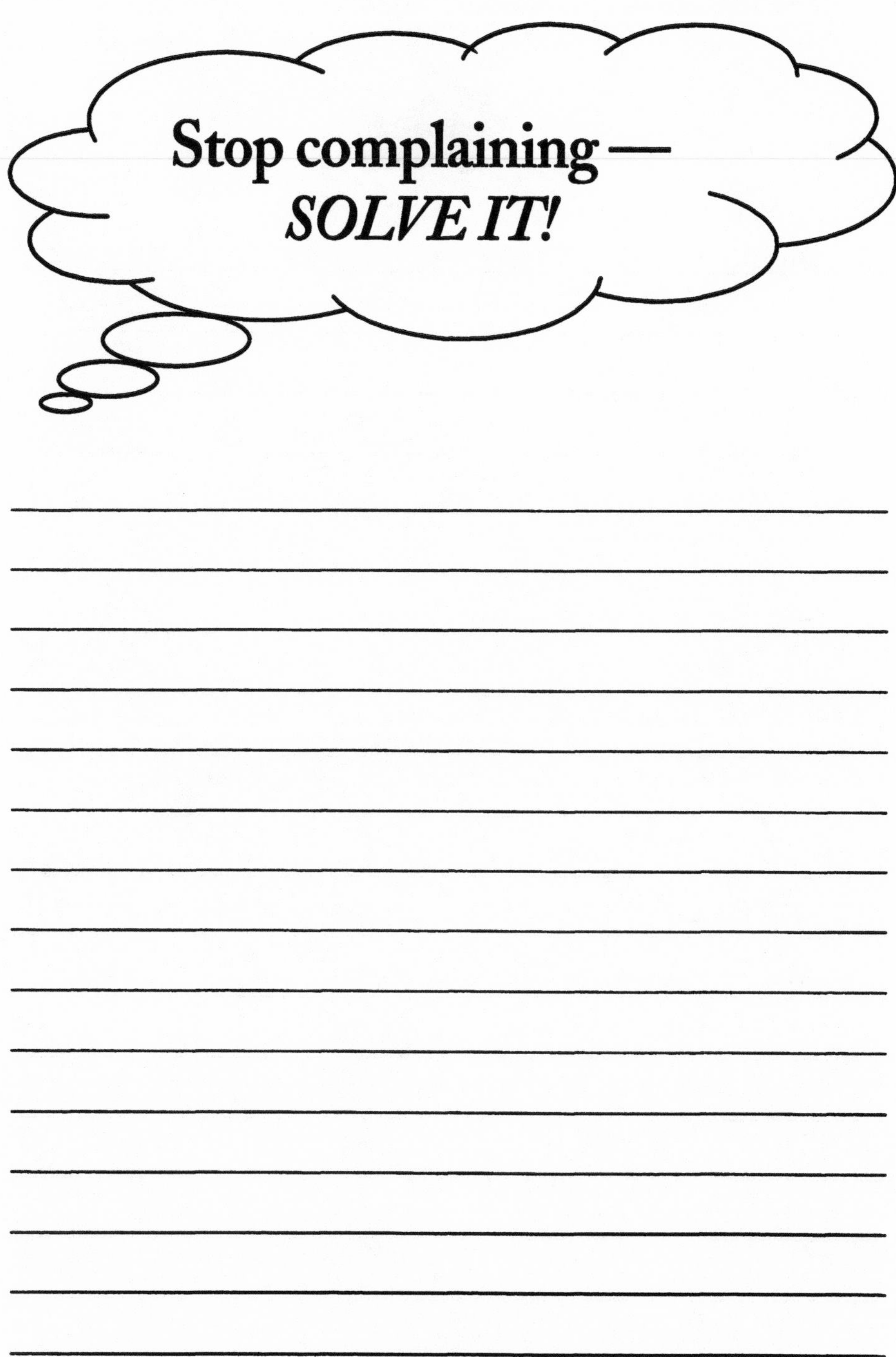
Stop complaining —
SOLVE IT!

LEARN and *GROW*
from your past!

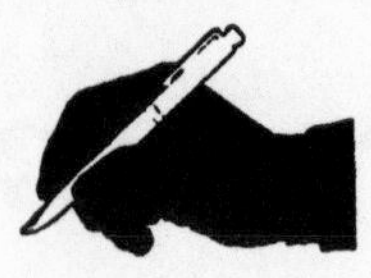

To learn more about this quote - refer to page 13

Are you LIVING
what you value?

To learn more about this quote - refer to pages 12, 20, 21

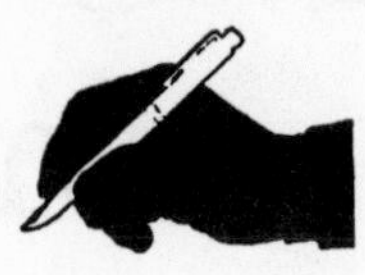

The Holiday

Splash the cologne,
Clean your home.
Ingredients, Invites.
No one's alone.
Joy that breaks hearts of stone.
IT'S YOUR OWN!

Pictures on the television.
Cannot draw your intuition,
Nor bring your expectations
 to fruition.

The holiday is . . .
 what you make
The holiday is . . .
 what you give . . .
Not What *You Take!*

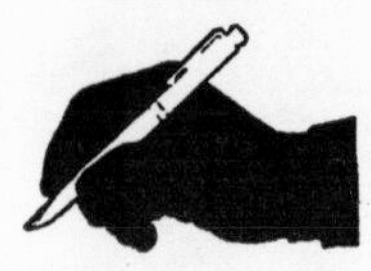

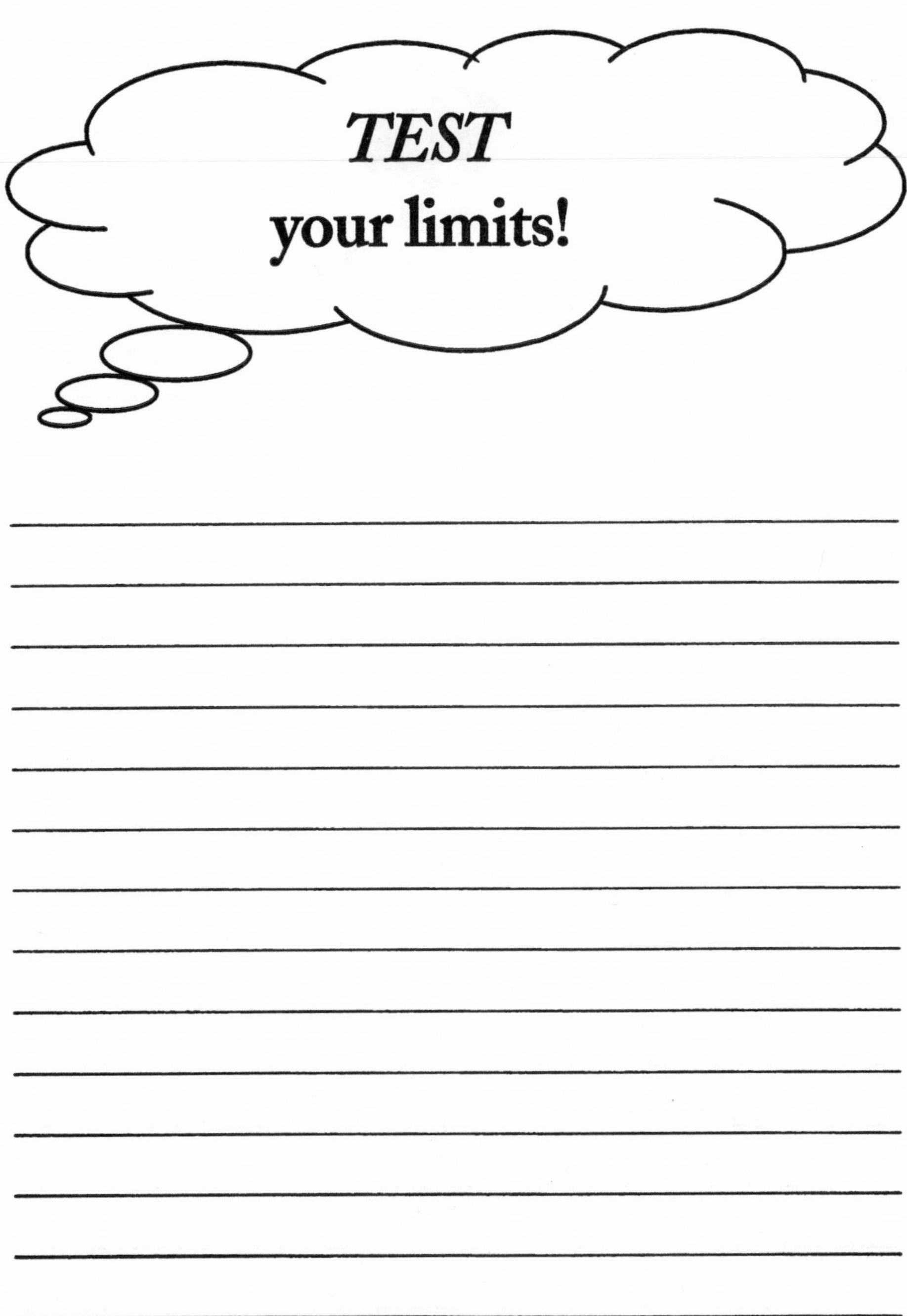

To learn more about this quote - refer to page 13

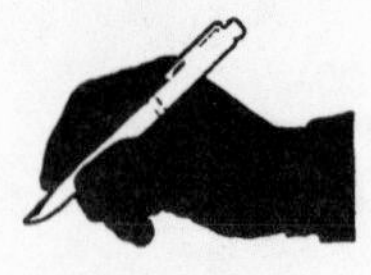

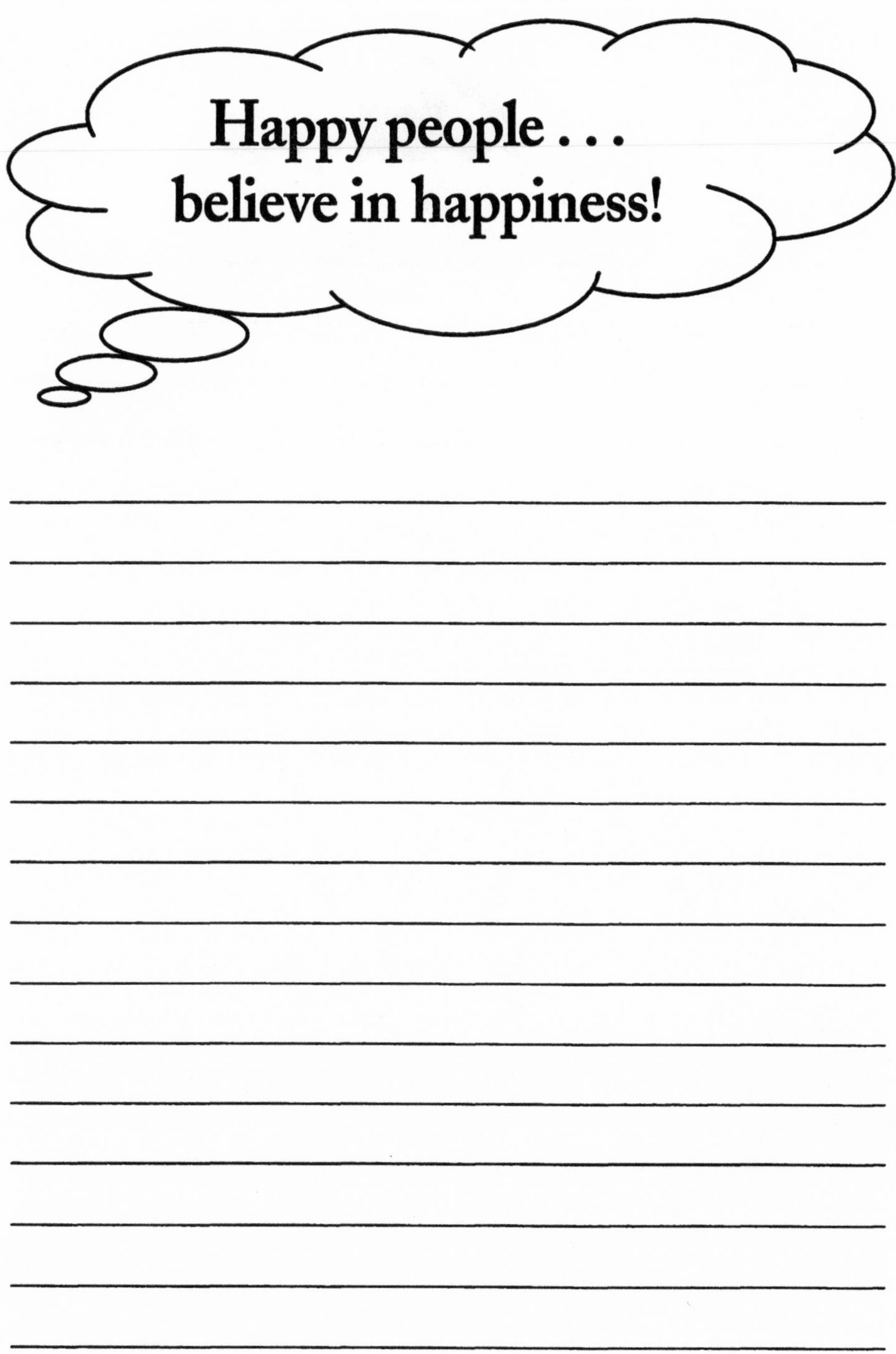
Happy people . . .
believe in happiness!

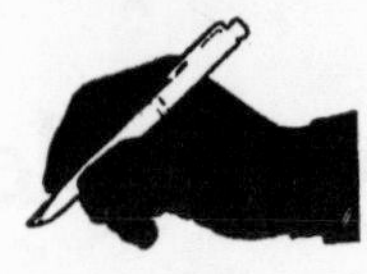

Material things
should never be valued
more than people.

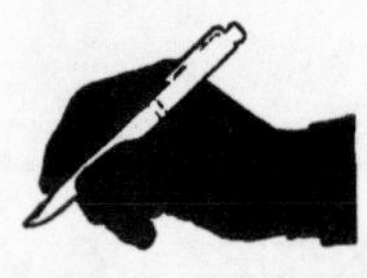

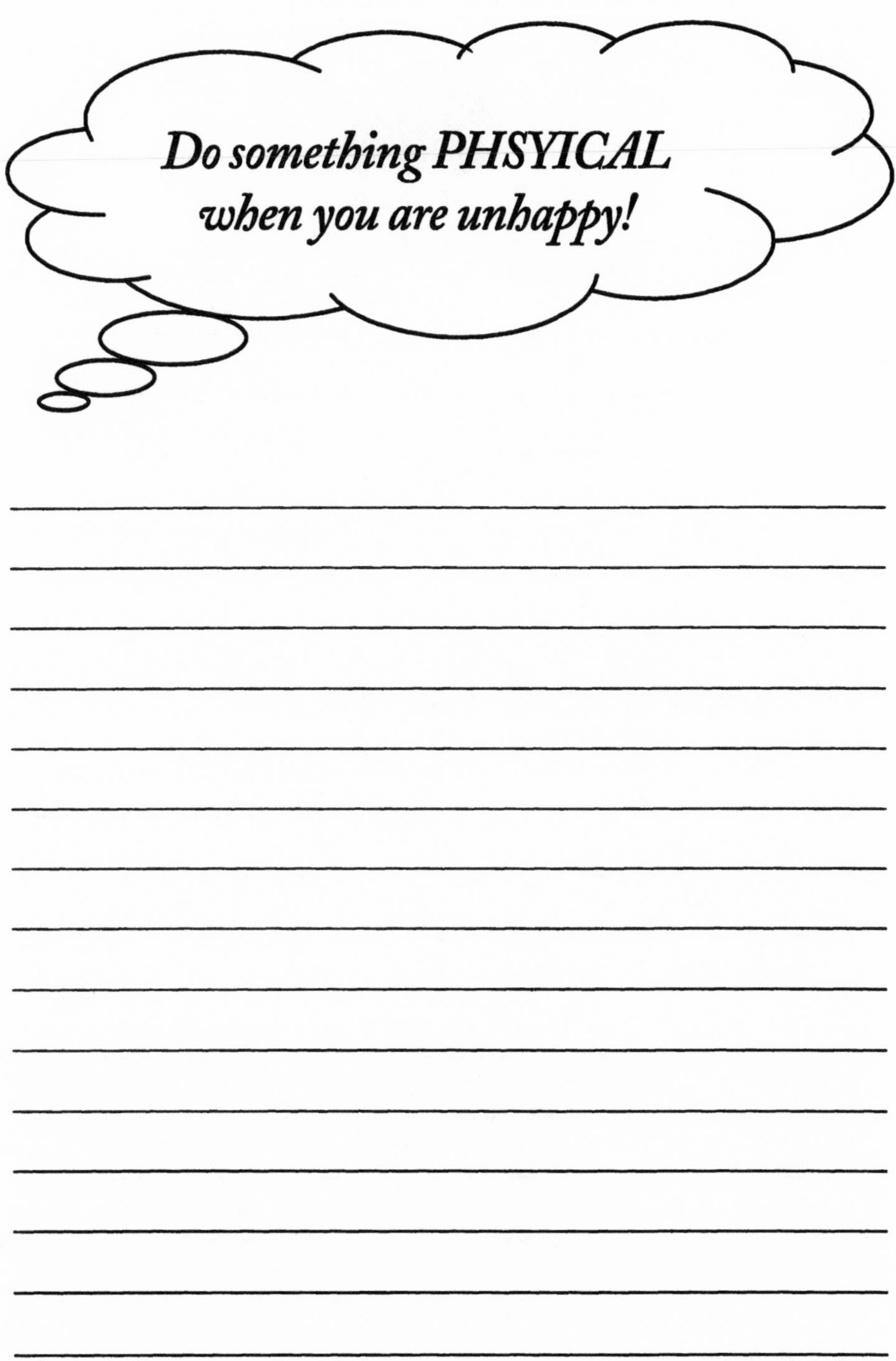
Do something PHSYICAL
when you are unhappy!

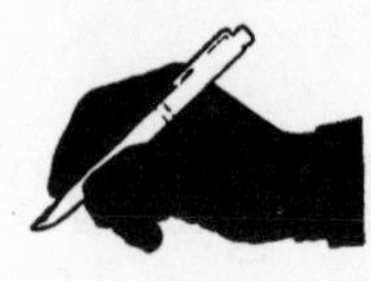

Happiness is based
on *YOUR* thoughts!

To learn more about this quote - refer to page 15

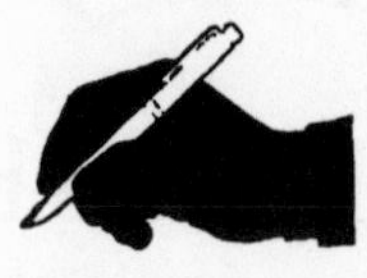

Sometimes . . .
there is no closure.

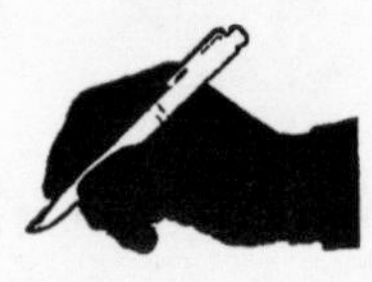

When is . . .
MORE better?

LESS . . .
may be better!

Physical activity
USES and CREATES
energy!

To learn more about this quote - refer to page 14

ONLY YOU
can control
your behavior!

To learn more about this quote - refer to page 15

A Birthday . . .

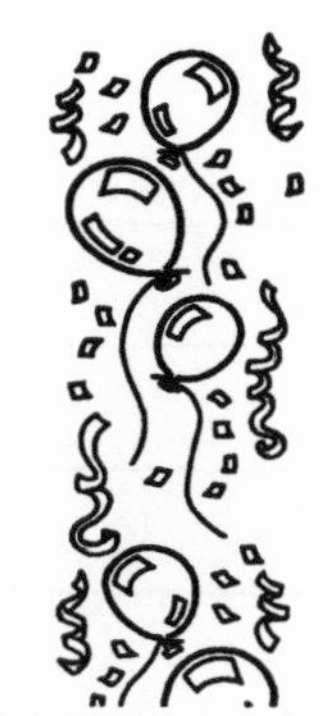

Is a day that talks to you
It is a day that walks with you
And whispers in your ear . . .
I'm so glad you're here!

Without a single scoop of ice cream
A candle blown, a first piece cut,
a dream,
Your Wish inside
From the world around you . . .
will beam!
Can you actually see it in the air?

Will friends and family be able to look
And not have to stare?
Is your wish so real . . .
Those who come to celebrate
Will eat it in their meal?
Yes! Yes! You they will feel!

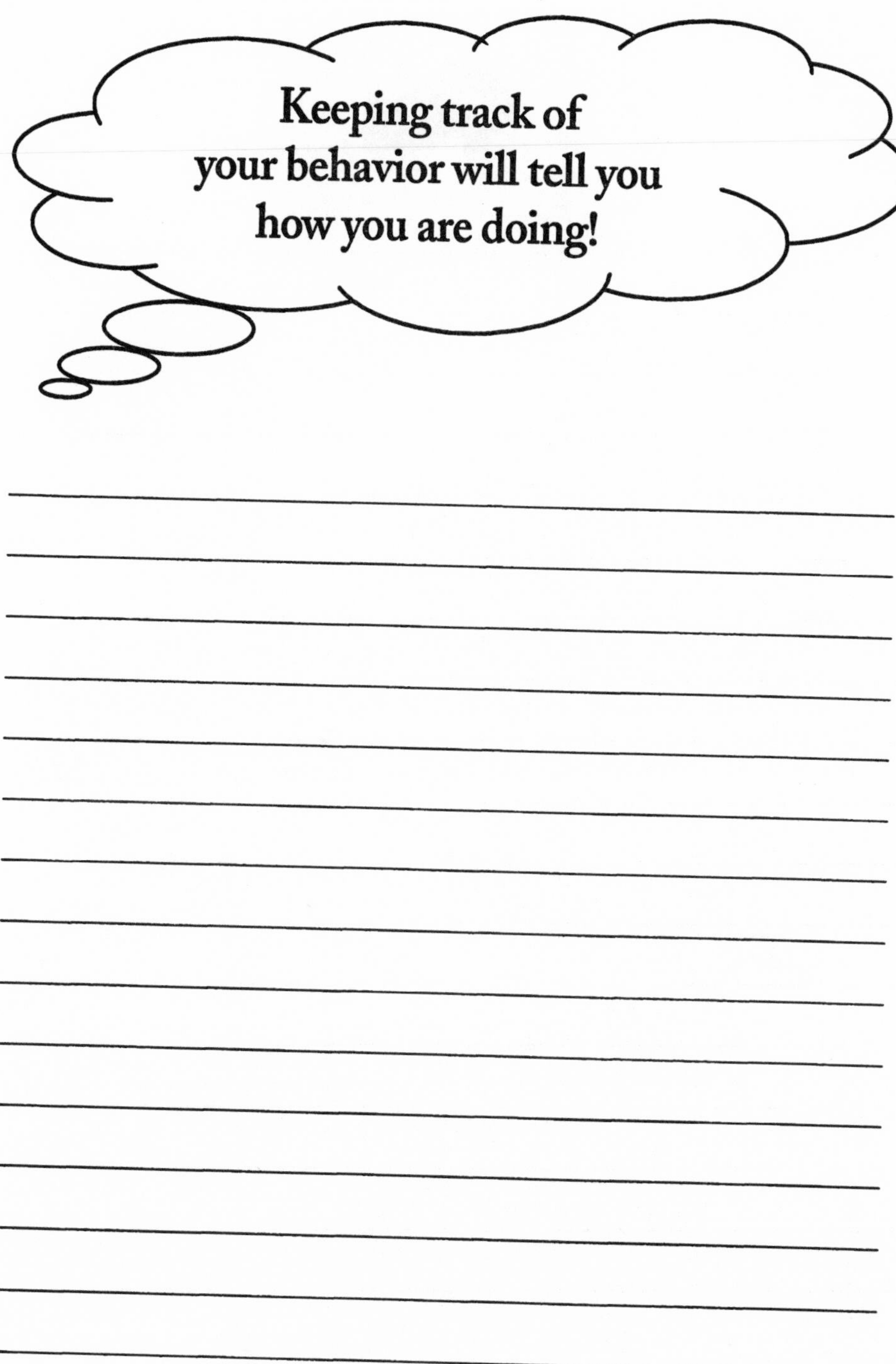
Keeping track of
your behavior will tell you
how you are doing!

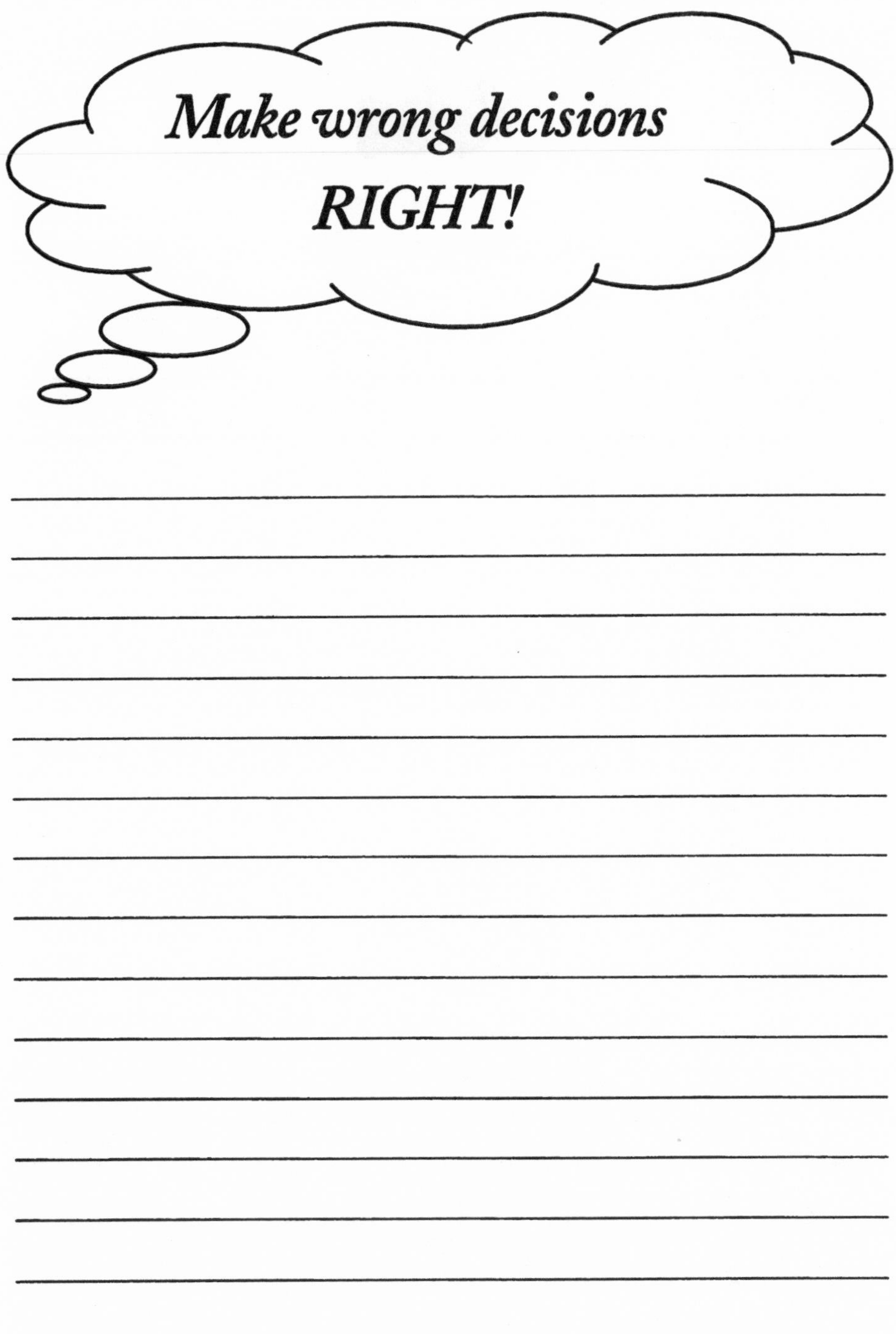
Make wrong decisions
RIGHT!

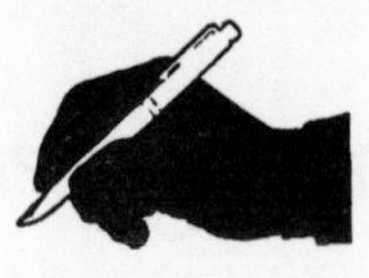

Knowledge + no action
= just knowledge!

SOLVE your problems
rather than endure them!

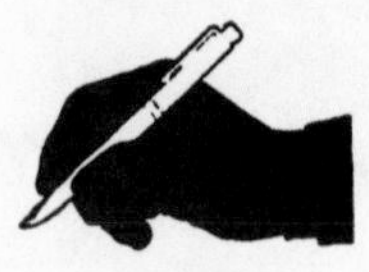

Don't say NO
for the other person!

HONOR
your word!

The person you spend
the most time with
is YOU.

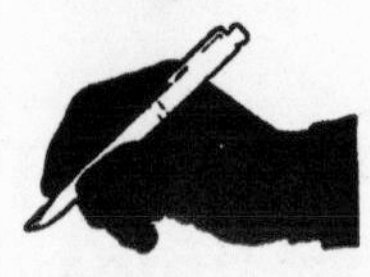

Are you digging the
WRONG ditch?

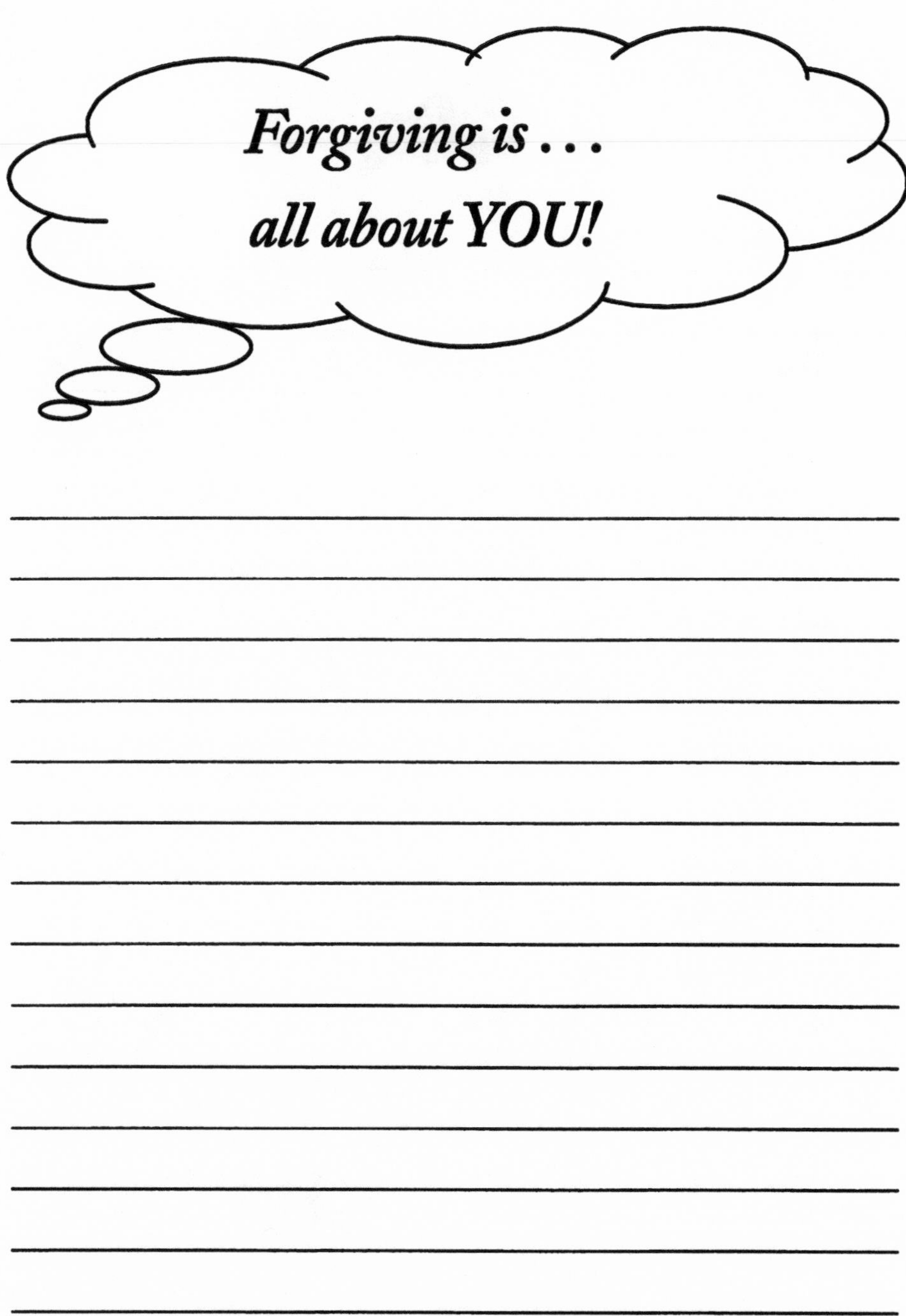
Forgiving is . . .
all about YOU!

To learn more about this quote - refer to pages 16, 17

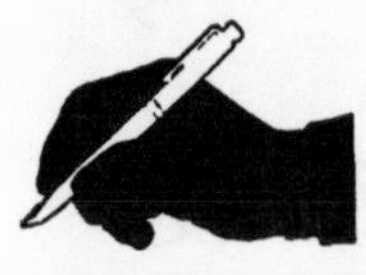

THINK!!!!

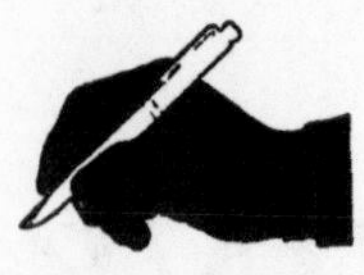

Graduation Day:
You wait and wait and wait . . .

Do not wait
To Graduate.

Wake up to your first alarm.
Carry another book in your arm.
And remember . . .
Despite sleep, worry, and work
An all-nighter does no harm.

Love it. Read it. Love it.
Gather your thoughts.

Put on your best suit
Or your best dress,
And leave behind all the rest.

Count each time you had to pay.
Going out of your way . . .
an extra hour not at home
an extra hour up late, alone.
You certainly would stay!

Run away. Run away.
And enjoy This Day.

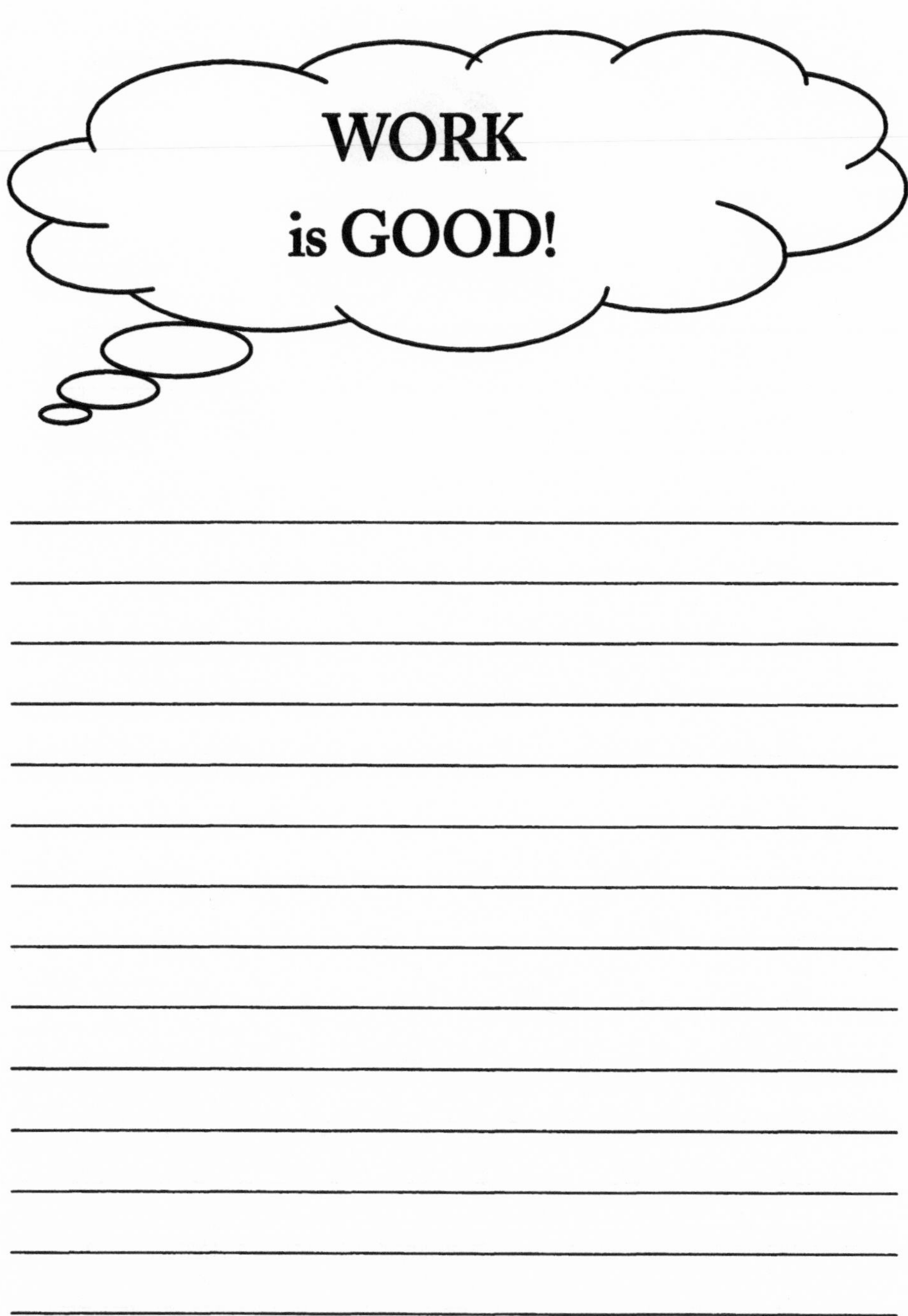

To learn more about this quote - refer to pages 20, 21

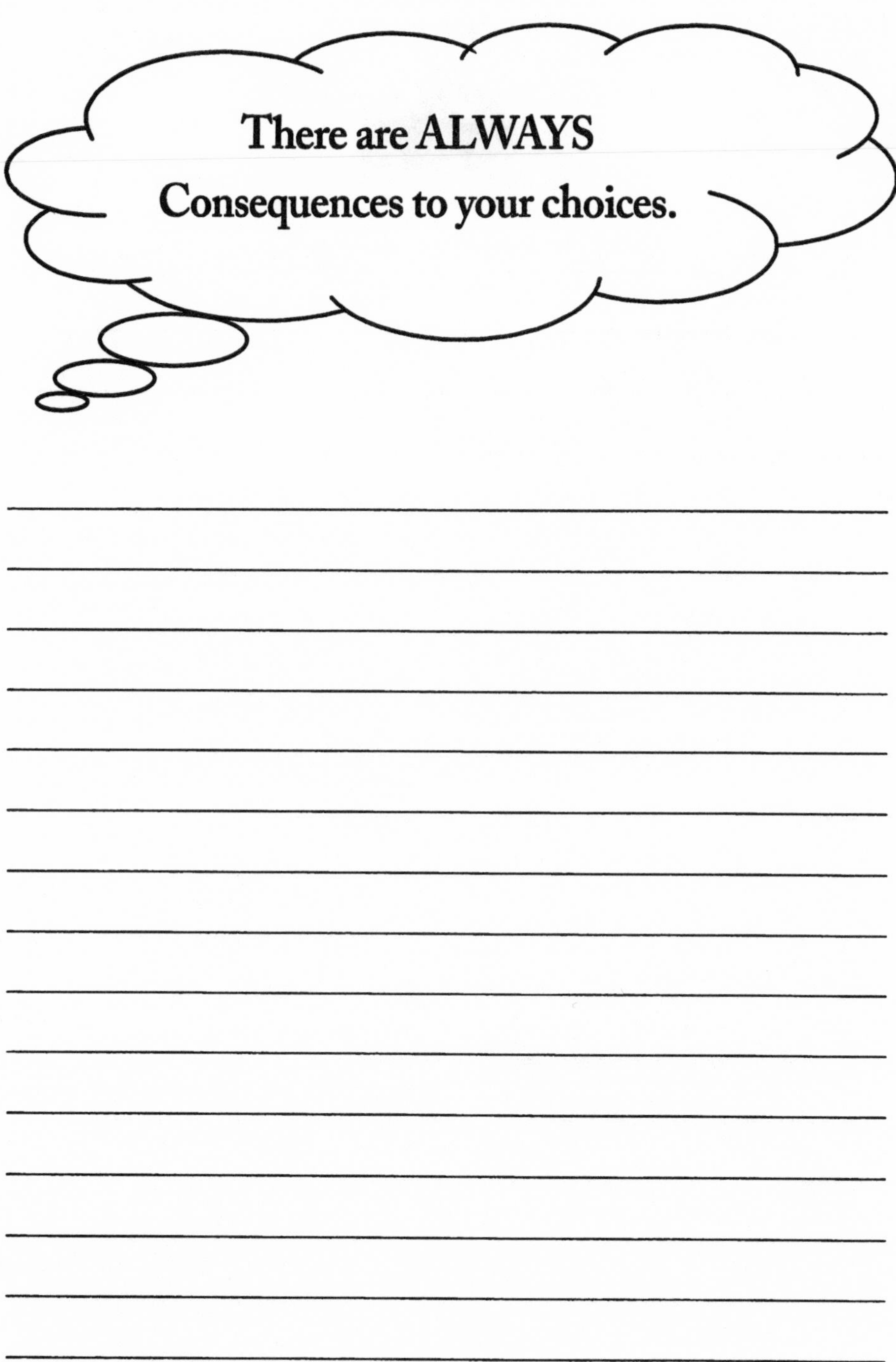
There are ALWAYS
Consequences to your choices.

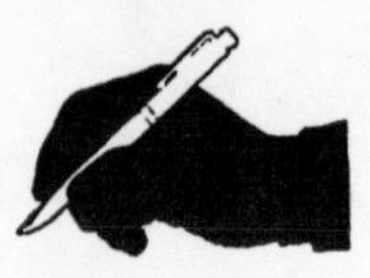

What isn't working . . .
CHANGE!

To learn more about this quote - refer to page 18

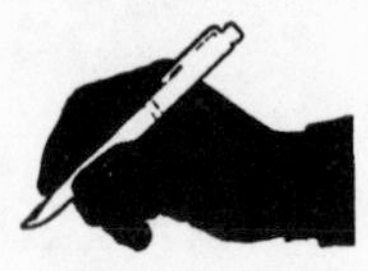

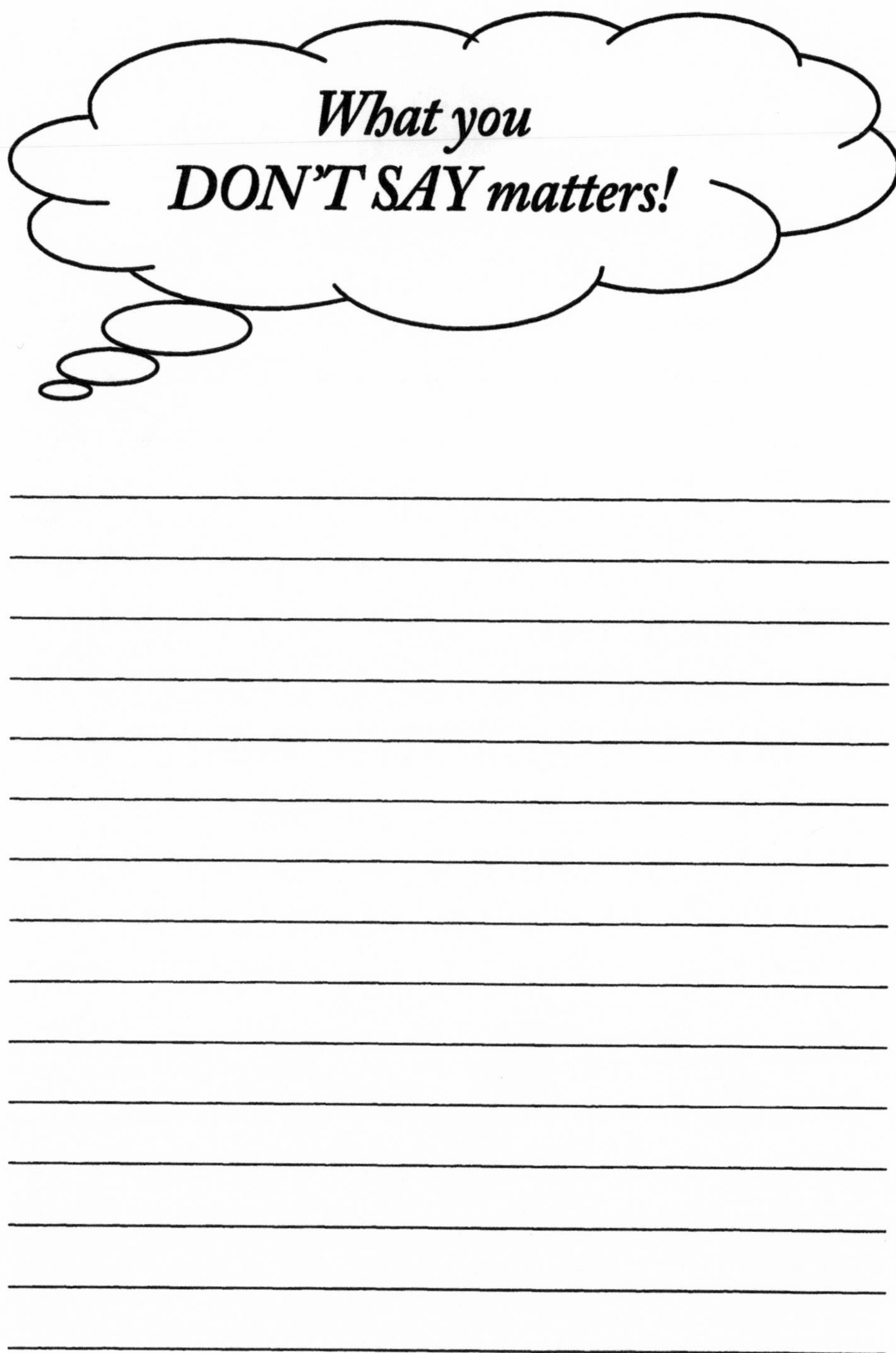
What you
DON'T SAY matters!

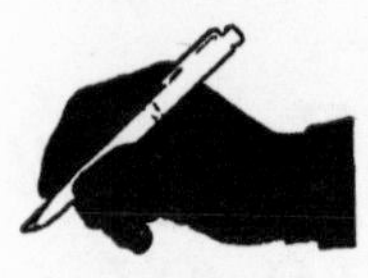

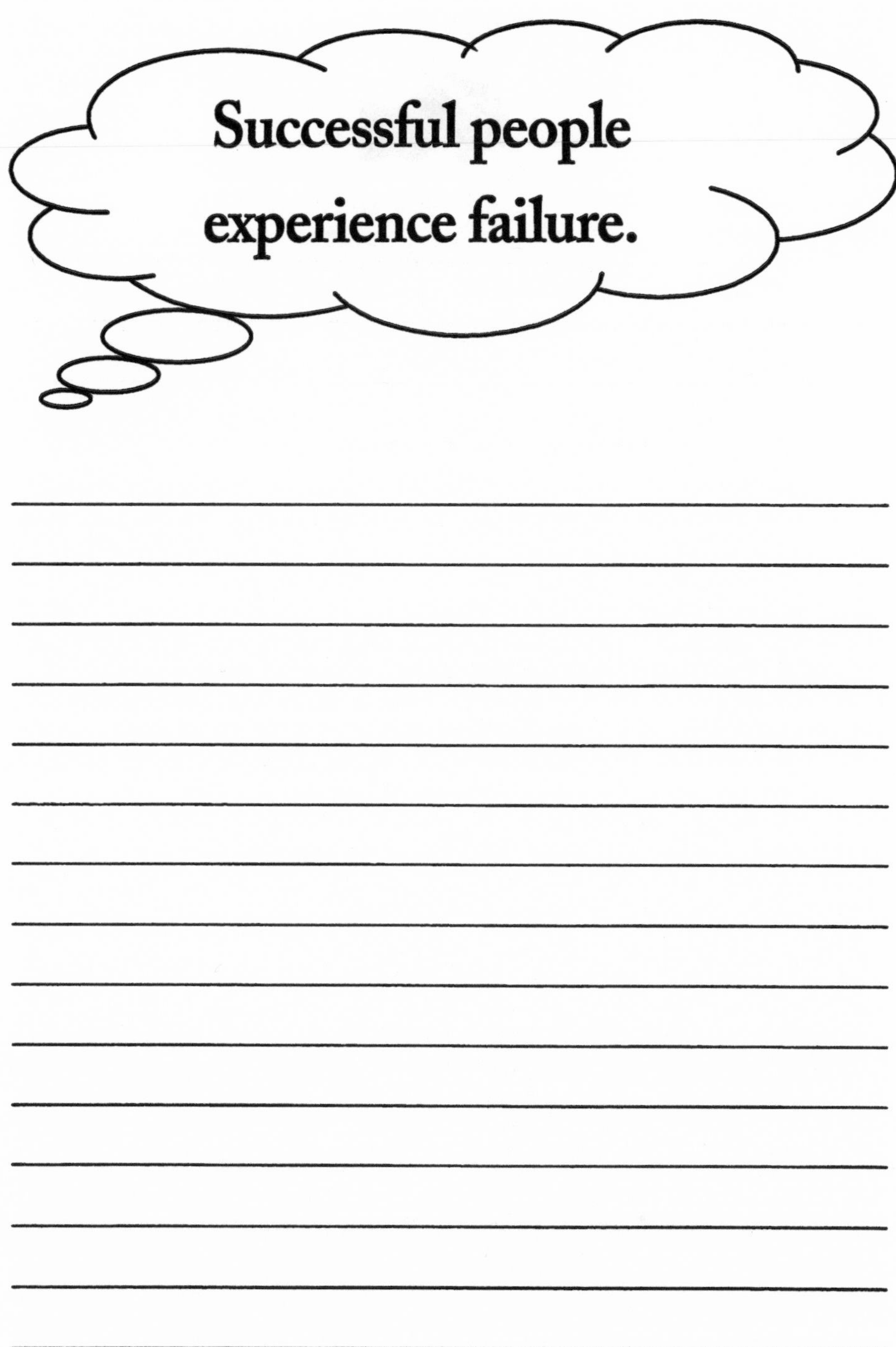
Successful people
experience failure.

When you LEARN
from failure,
it is an Accomplishment.

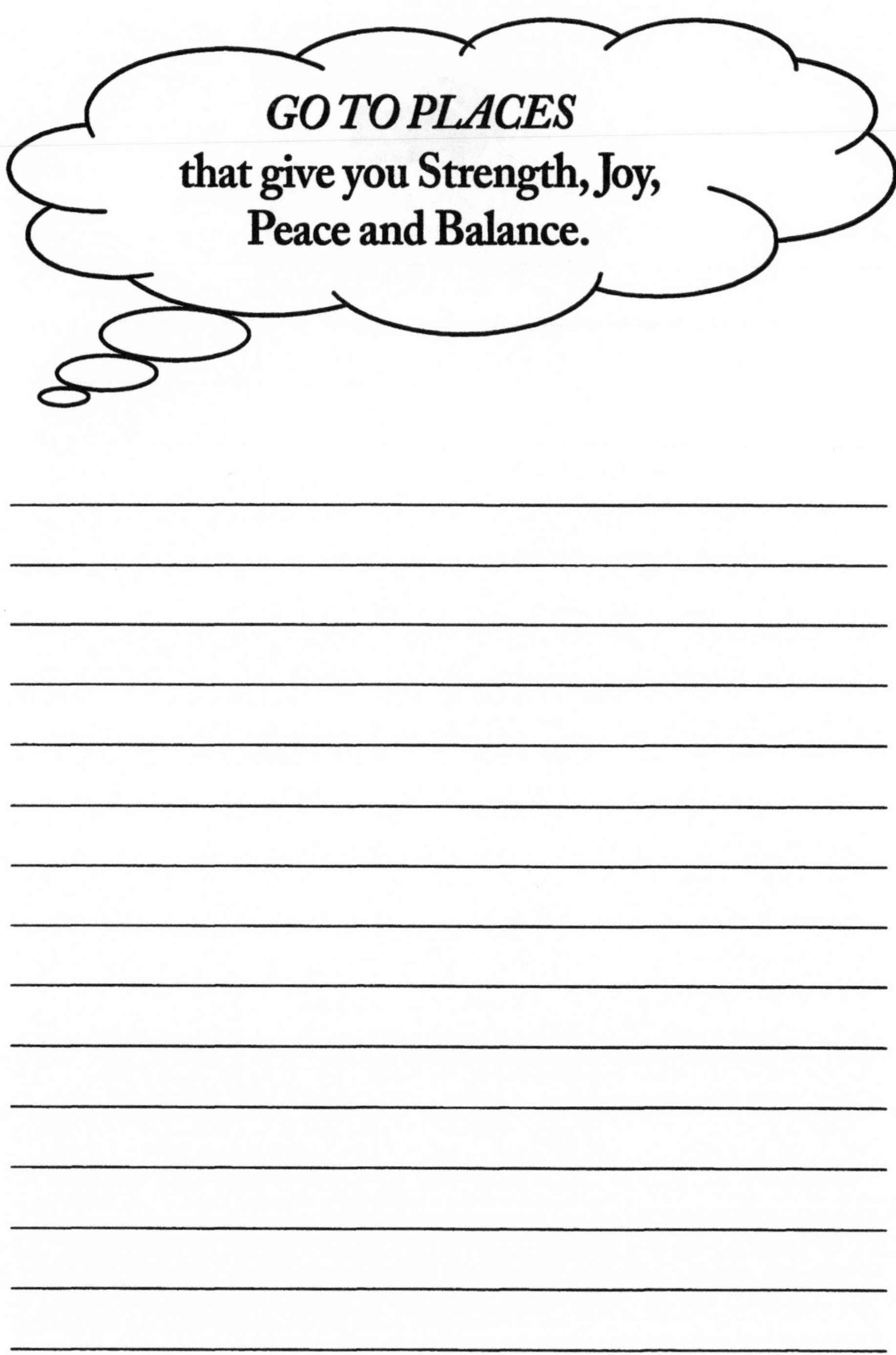
GO TO PLACES
that give you Strength, Joy,
Peace and Balance.

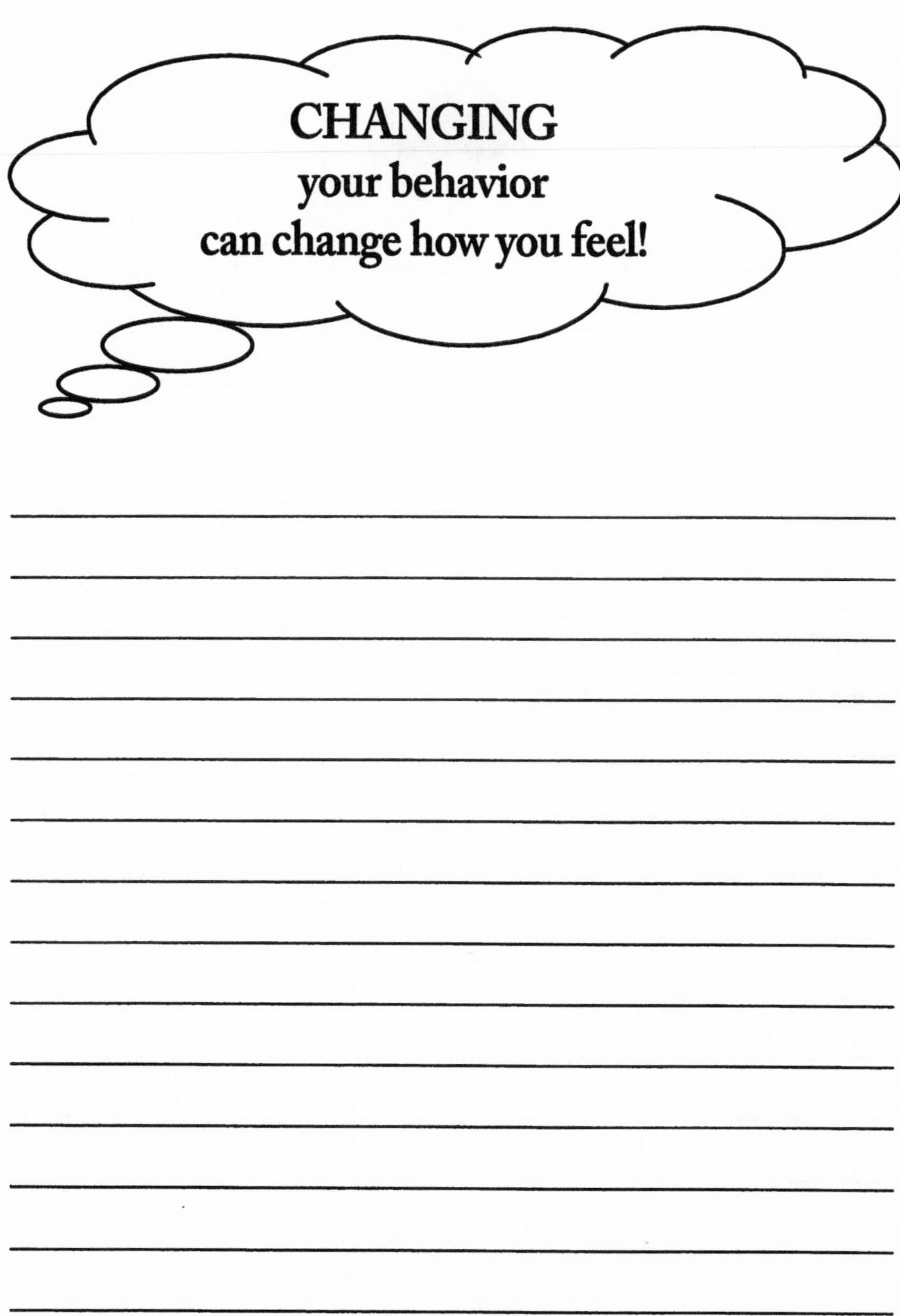
CHANGING
your behavior
can change how you feel!

To learn more about this quote - refer to page 18

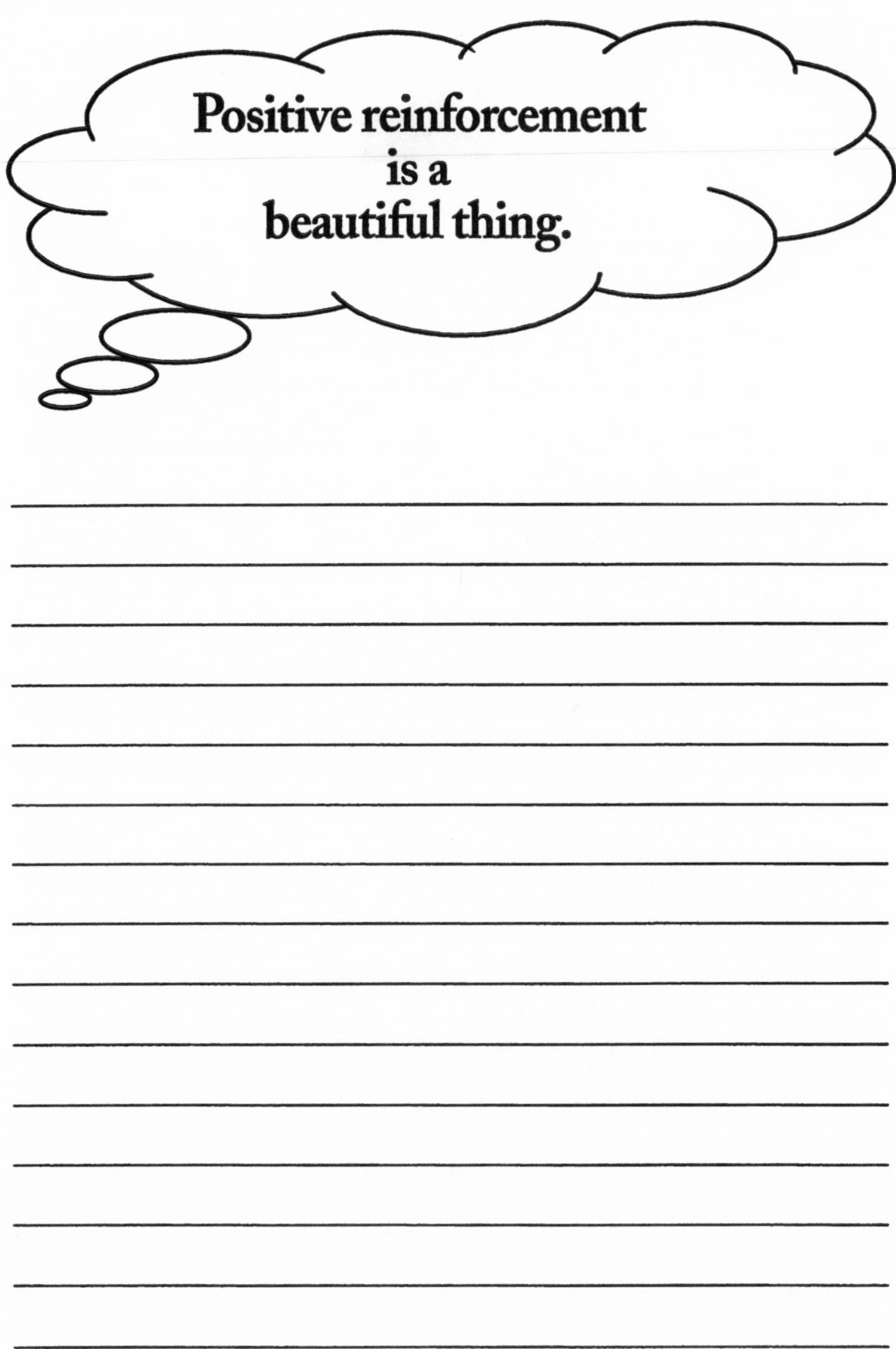
Positive reinforcement
is a
beautiful thing.

The happiest times in your
life are when you are
with people you love.

A Wedding Exactly Yours

Exactly . . .
Is the word you say
Long before the actual day.
When someone can speak your dreams
Where they can visit your past it seems.

Love knows the way.
Exactly . . .
Shoulder to Shoulder
Exactly . . .
Growing Older
Exactly . . .
Heart to Heart
Exactly . . .
2 in 1 at the Start

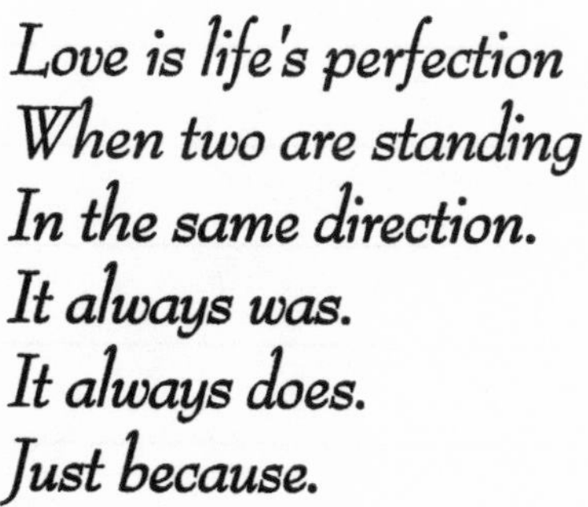

Love is life's perfection
When two are standing
In the same direction.
It always was.
It always does.
Just because.

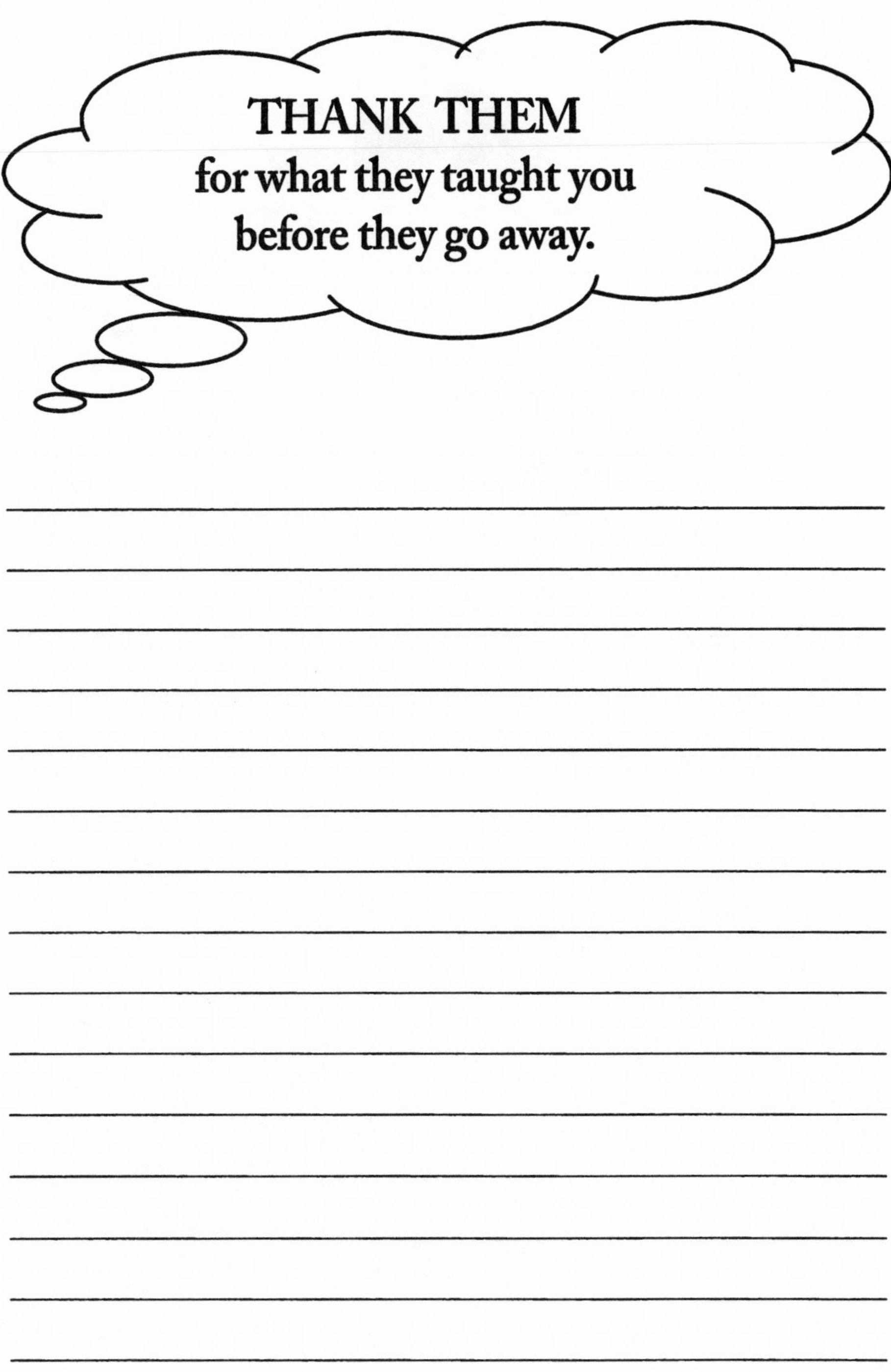
THANK THEM
for what they taught you
before they go away.

What you
SAY matters!

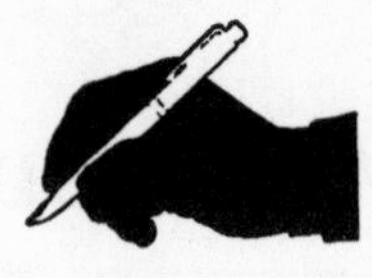

Life is short!

Focus on MOVING FORWARD!

To learn more about this quote - refer to page 19

Enjoy NOW!

ARE YOU DRIFTING?

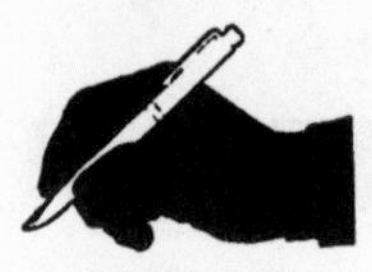

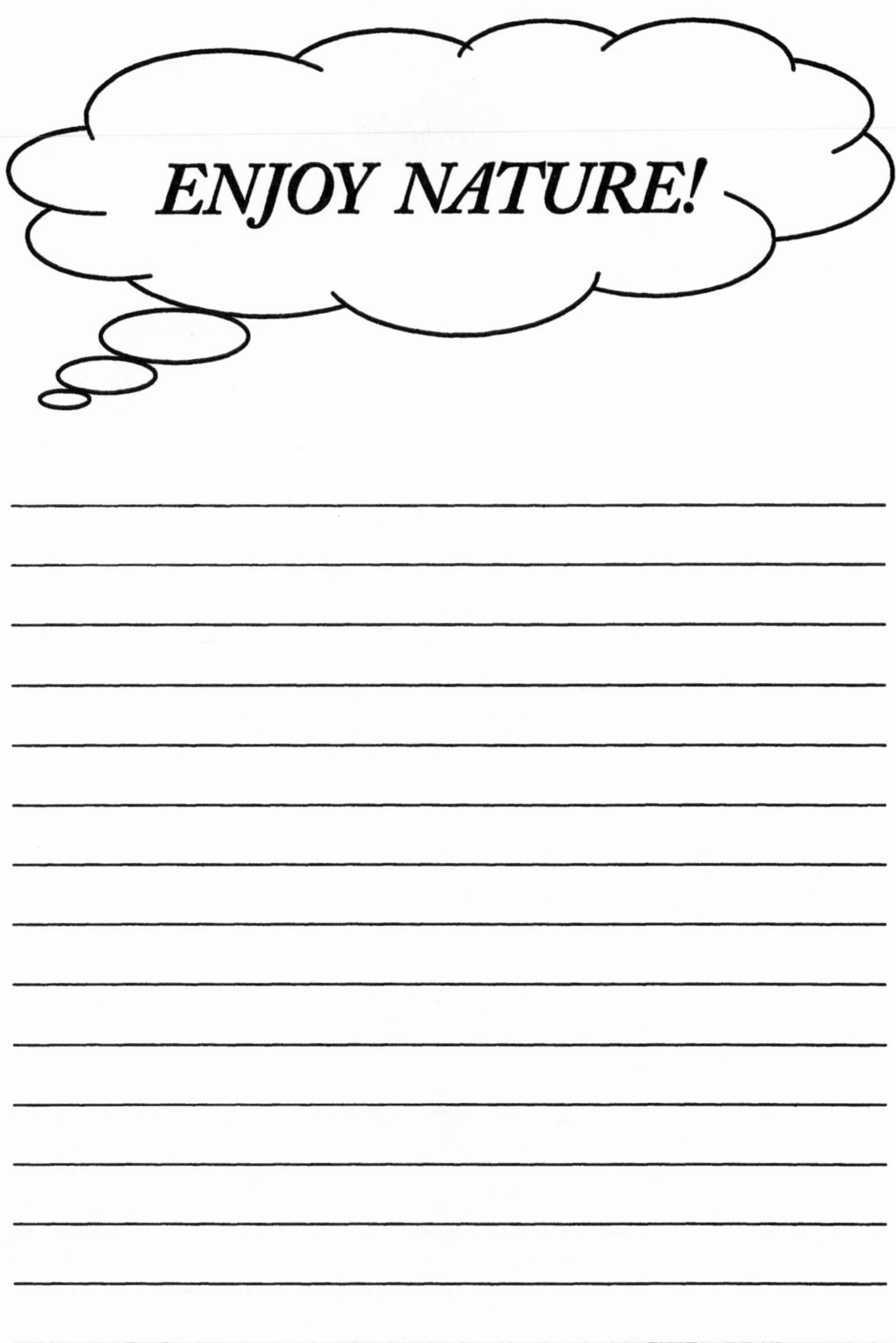
ENJOY NATURE!

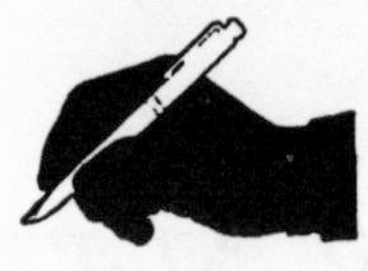

MANAGE
your life!

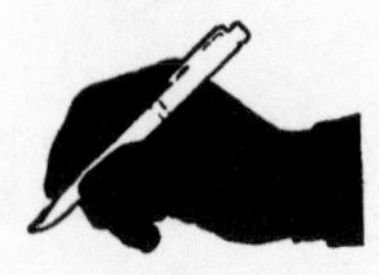

Sometimes . . .
IT IS
what it IS!

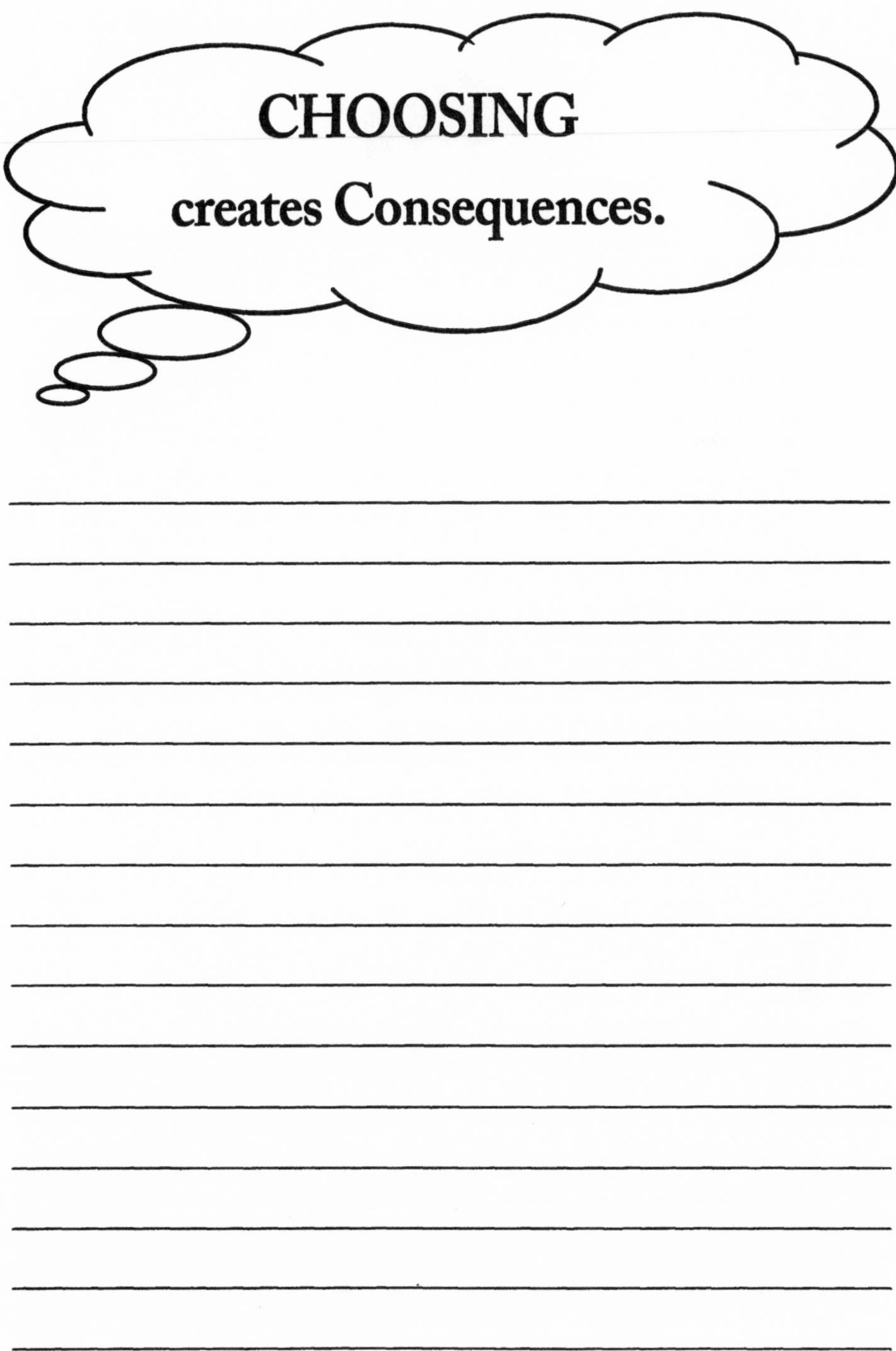
CHOOSING
creates Consequences.

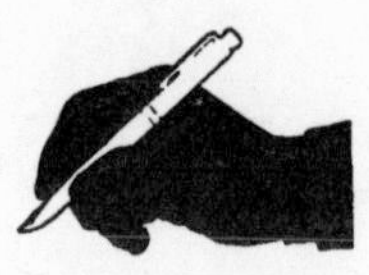

The Anniversary

Returns
The hours and minutes in a day!
In the same sensational way!

Is it possible
To not just feel,
But make the essence
        of a moment, real?
So you can smell it again.

Look around
And you're exactly where you've been.
It answers not how
Not what nor why.

Only when.
Do not ask: Can?
When you trek down that trail.
Listen to the whistle
Open up the peanuts
And ride the rail!

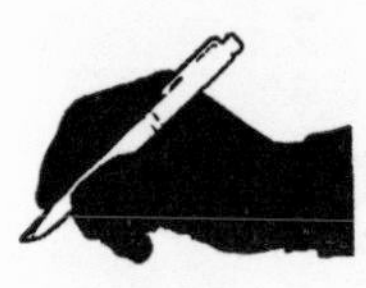

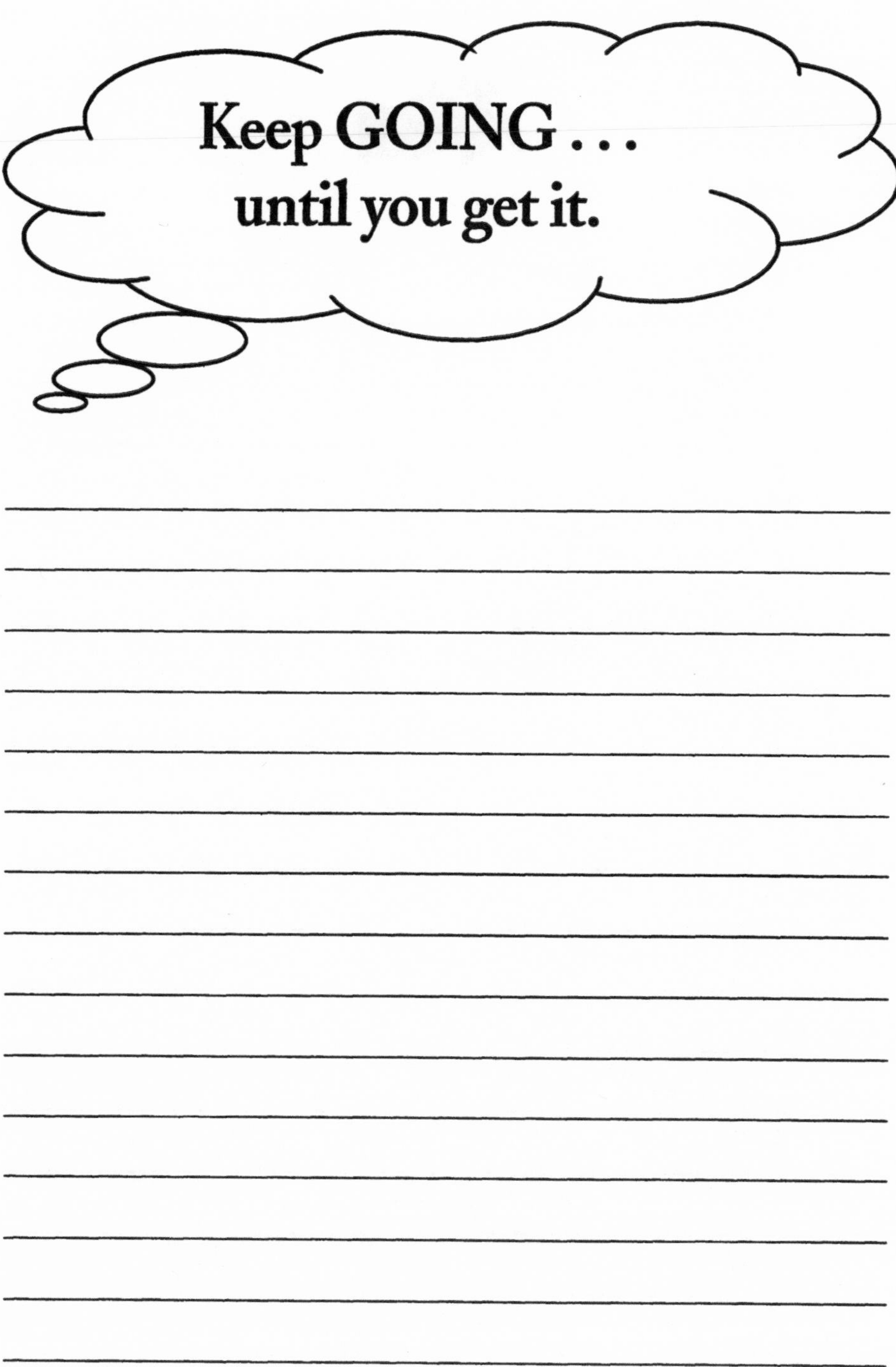
Keep GOING . . .
until you get it.

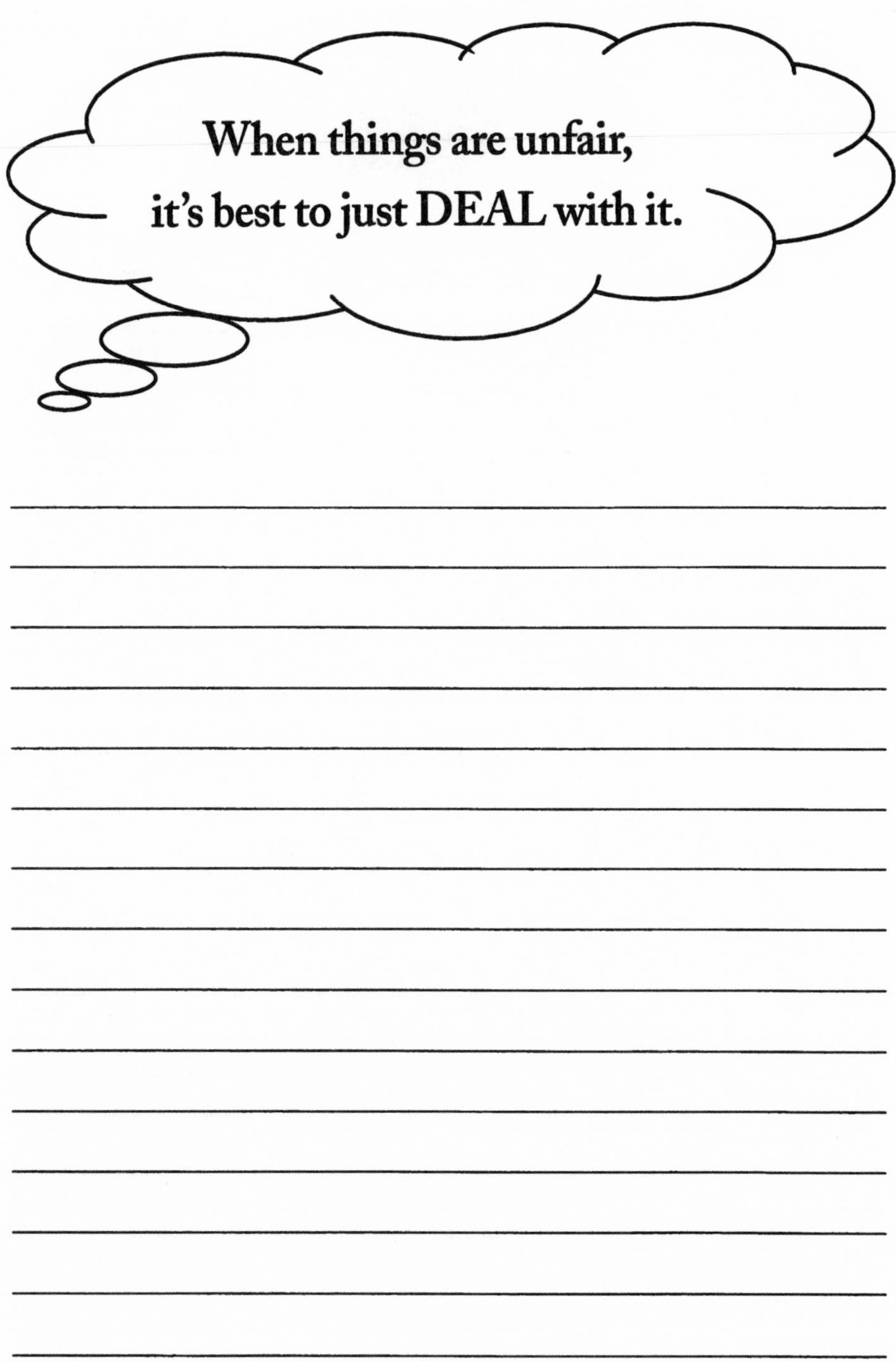
When things are unfair,
it's best to just DEAL with it.

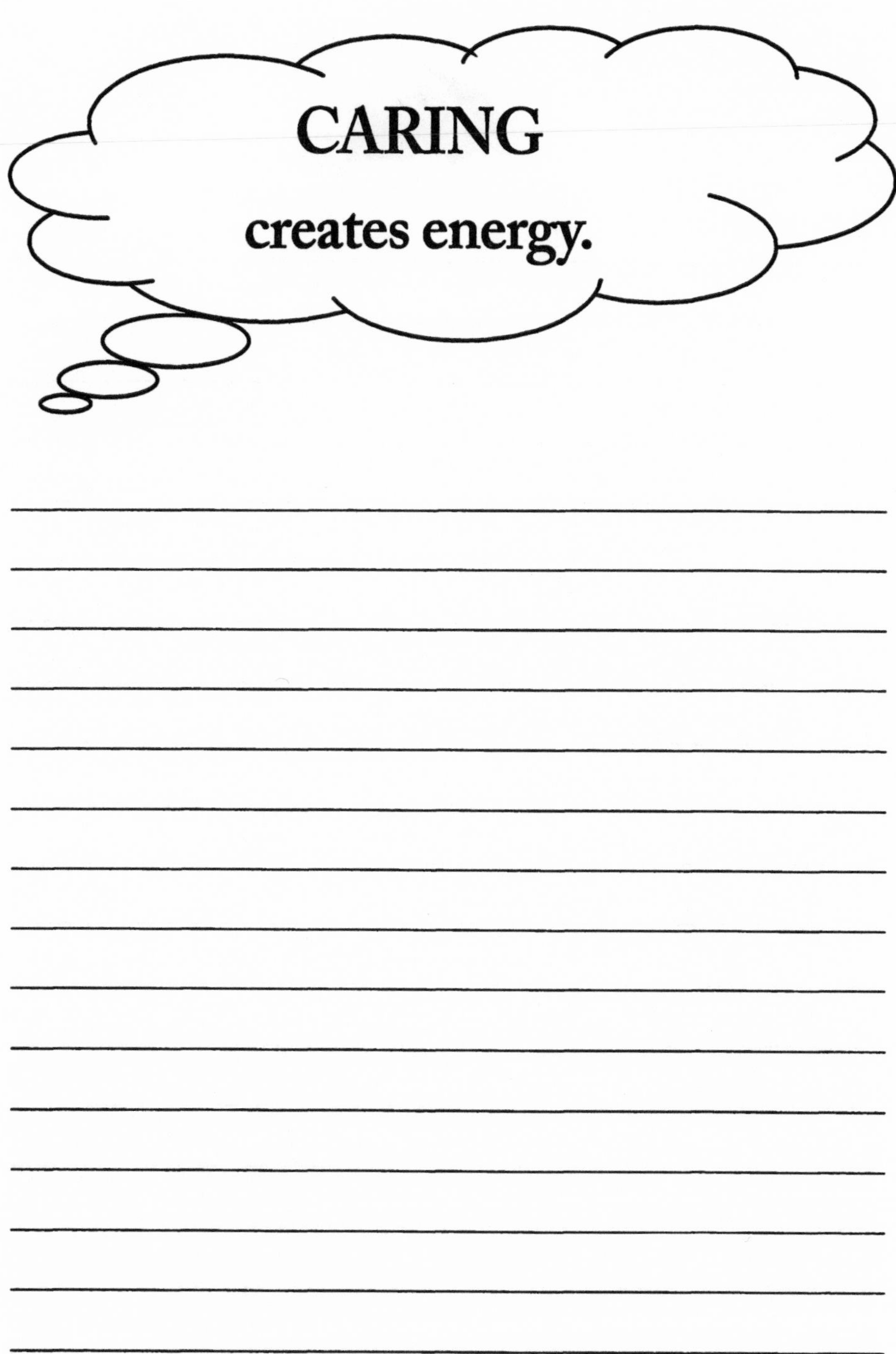
CARING
creates energy.

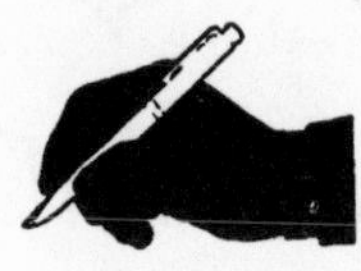

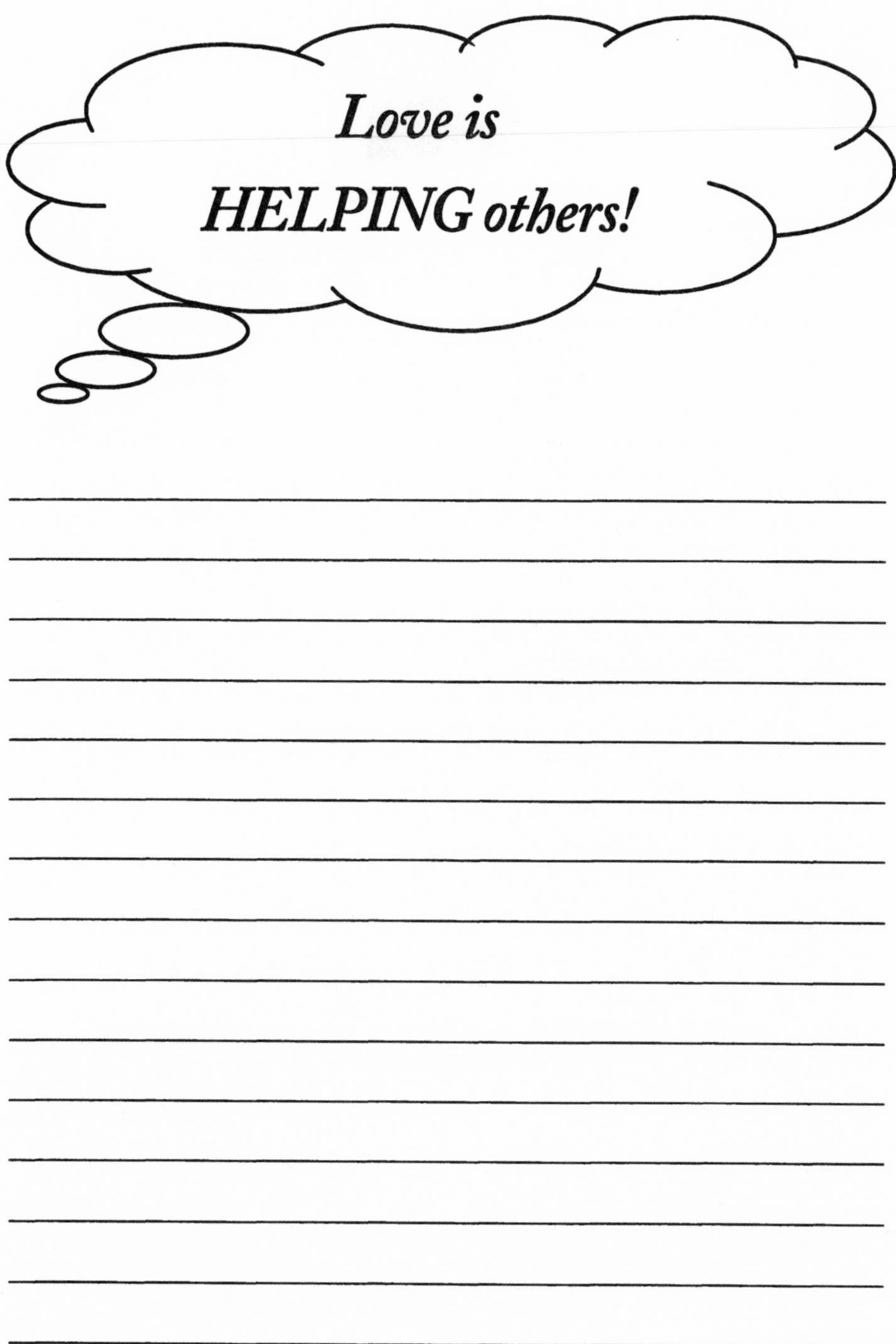
Love is
HELPING others!

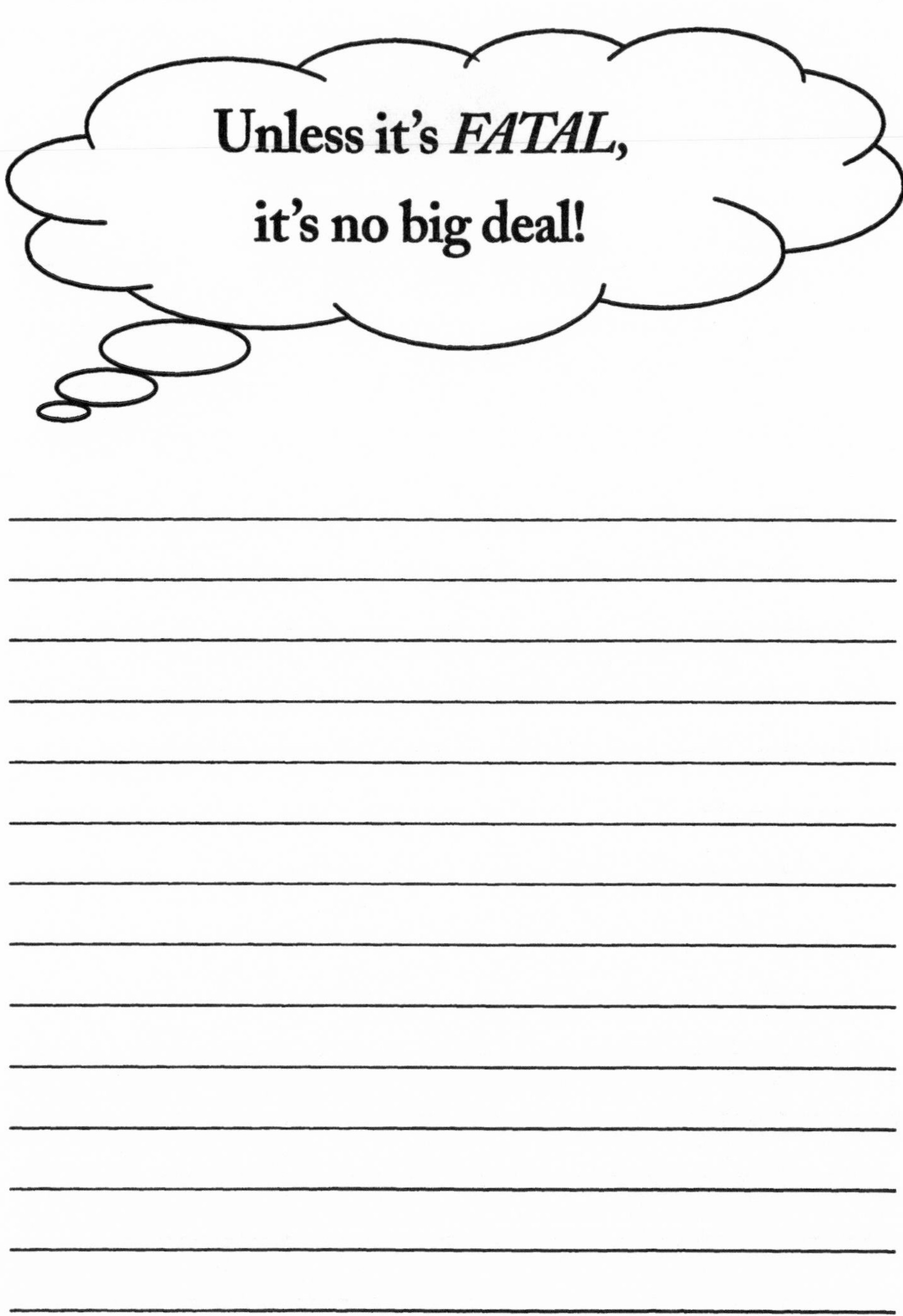
Unless it's *FATAL*,
it's no big deal!

To learn more about this quote - refer to pages 16, 17

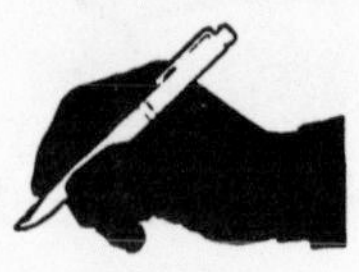

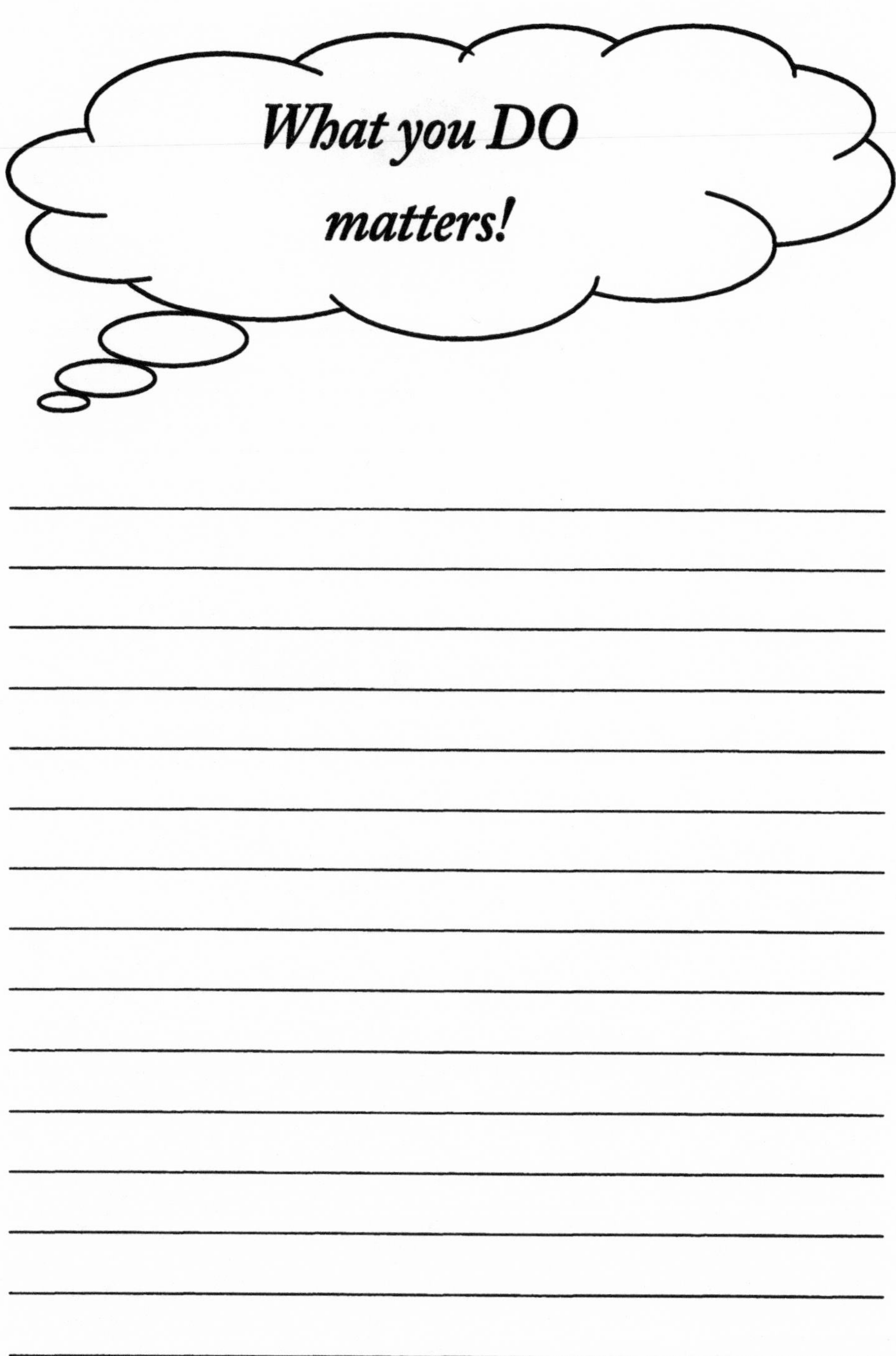
What you DO
matters!

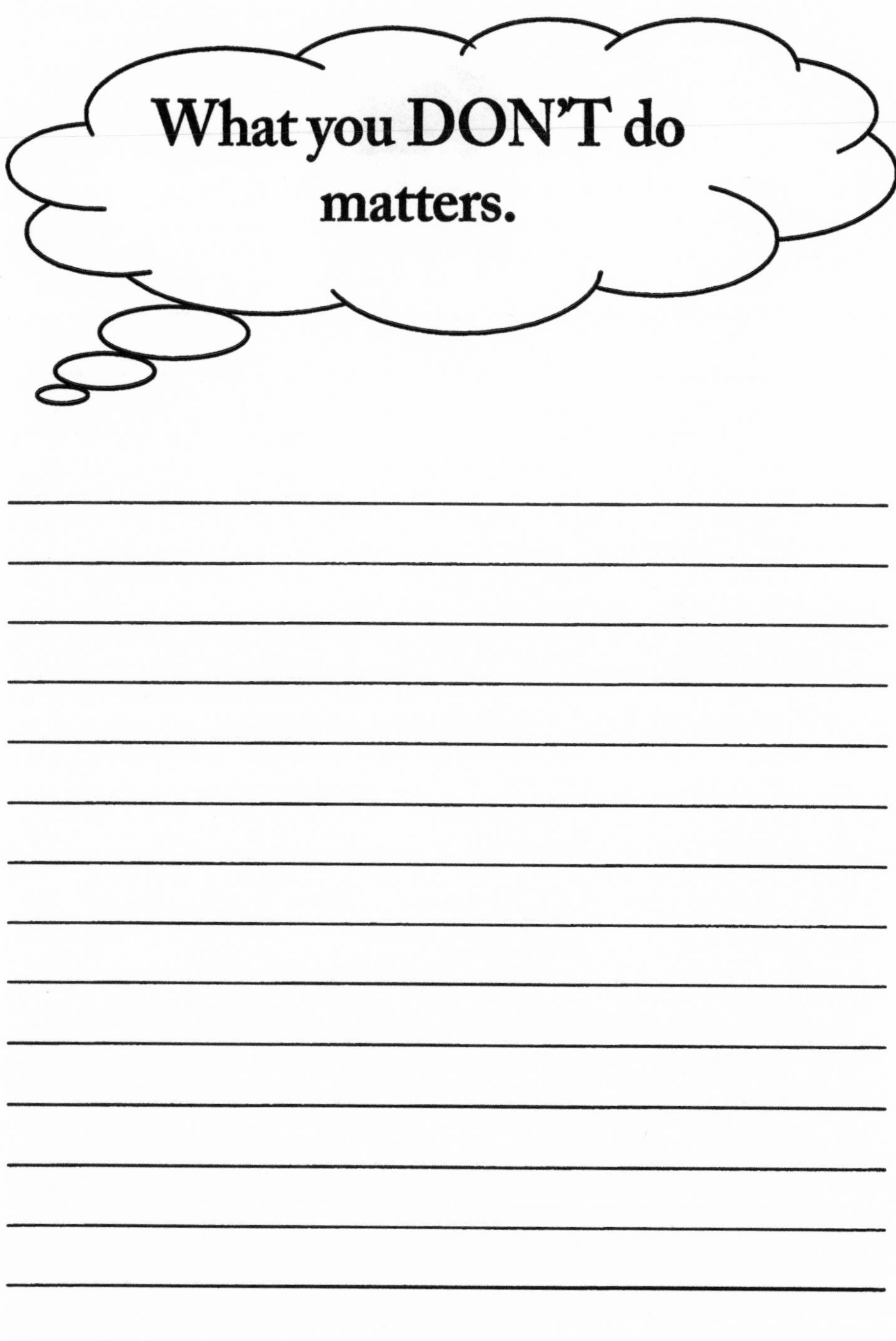
What you DON'T do
matters.

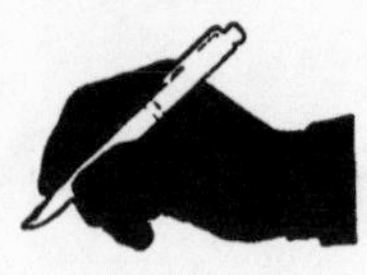

TRUTH
creates energy!

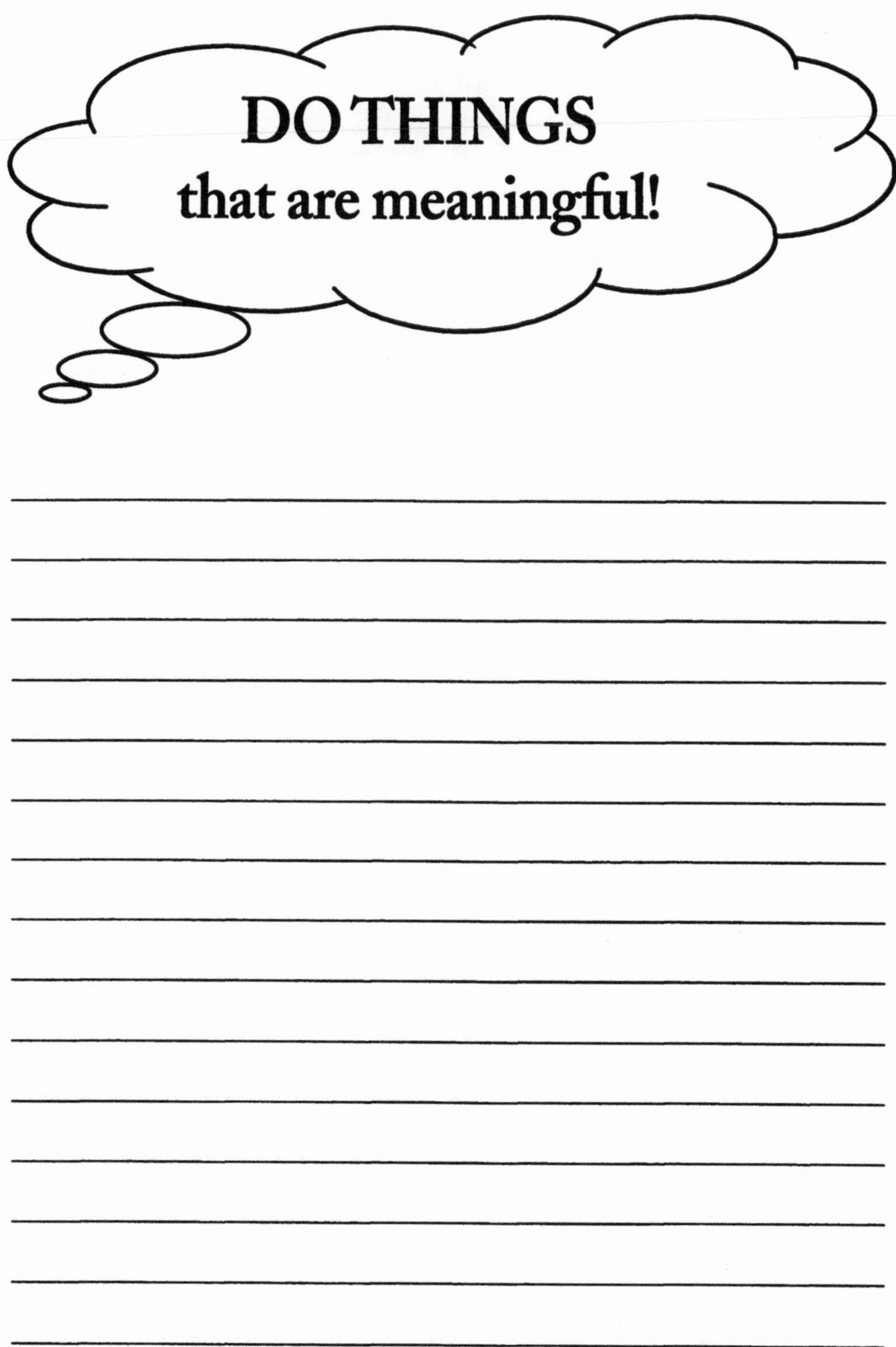
DO THINGS
that are meaningful!

To learn more about this quote - refer to pages 20, 21

Retirement Starts . . .
When You Start

Too many years of stopping
For when someone says, "Get down,"
You've done your share of dropping.

Now you can stand.
Meet your own demand.
And lead your own band

With the music you'll discover
The notes that make your melody,
You will. Uncover!

What songs did I write?
What wrongs did I right?
What symphonies are now in my sight?

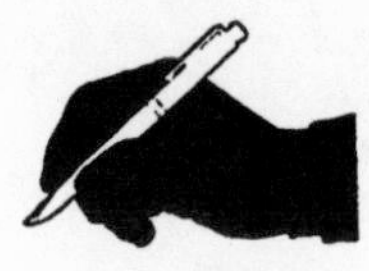

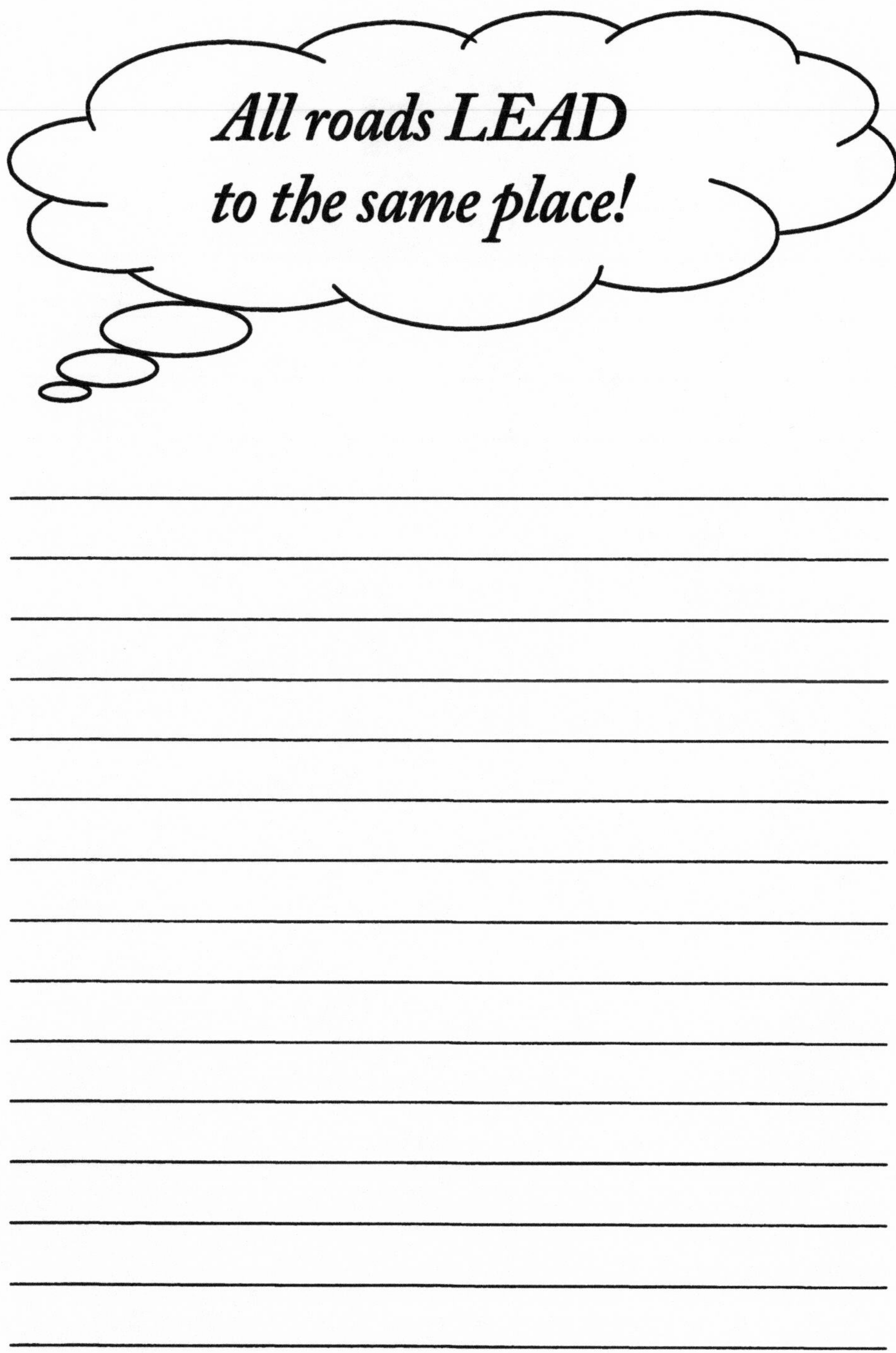
All roads LEAD
to the same place!

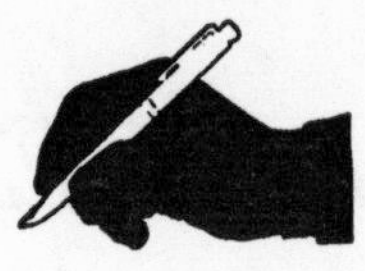

Are YOU in a rut?

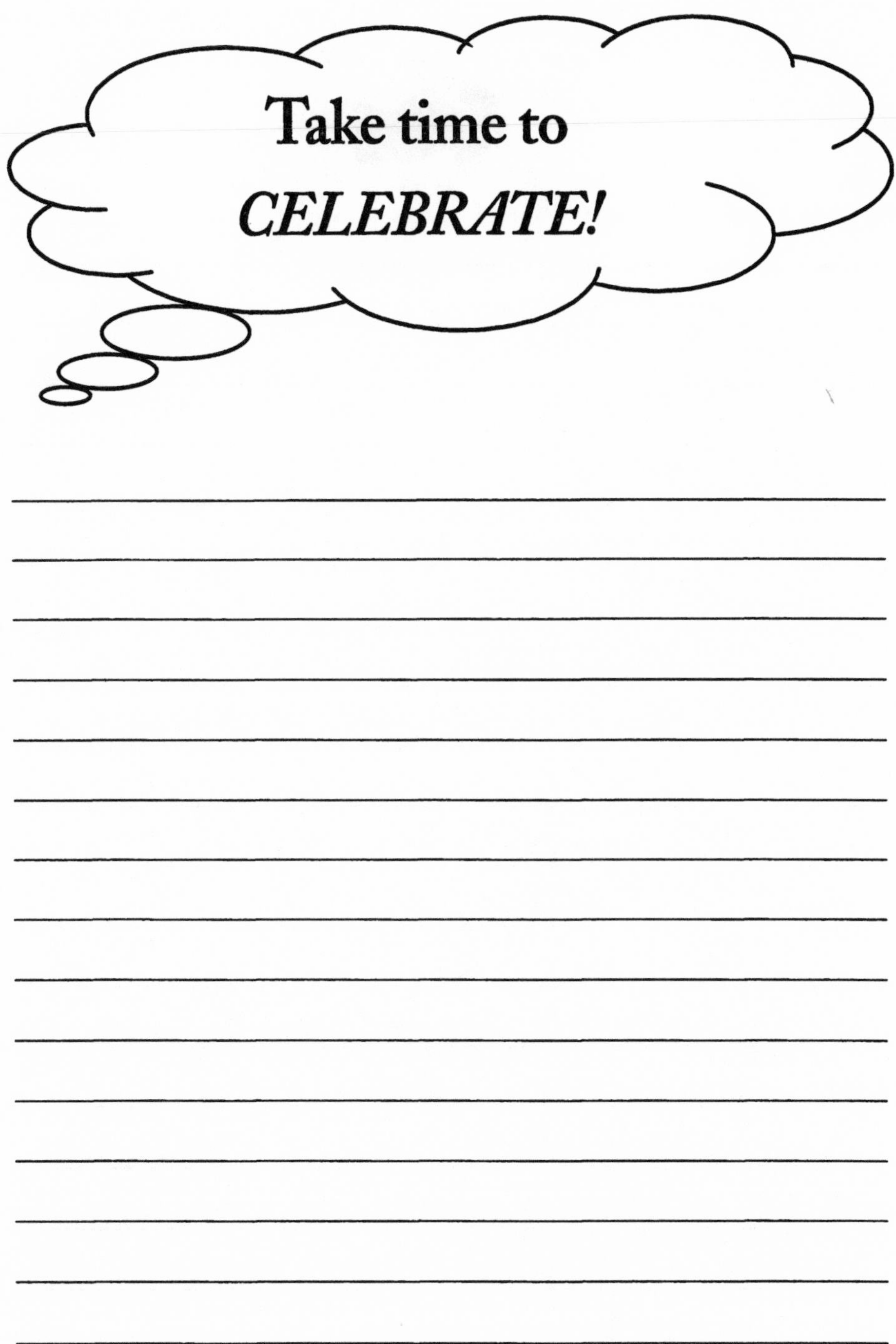
Take time to
CELEBRATE!

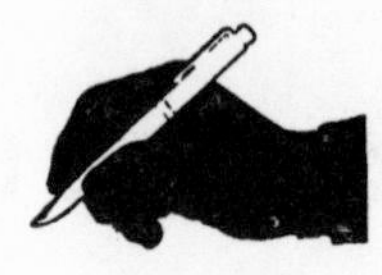

BE THERE!

To learn more about this quote - refer to page 13

Harmonize
family and work!

To learn more about this quote - refer to pages 20, 21

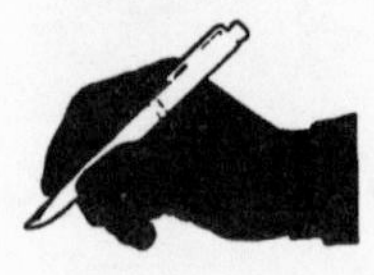

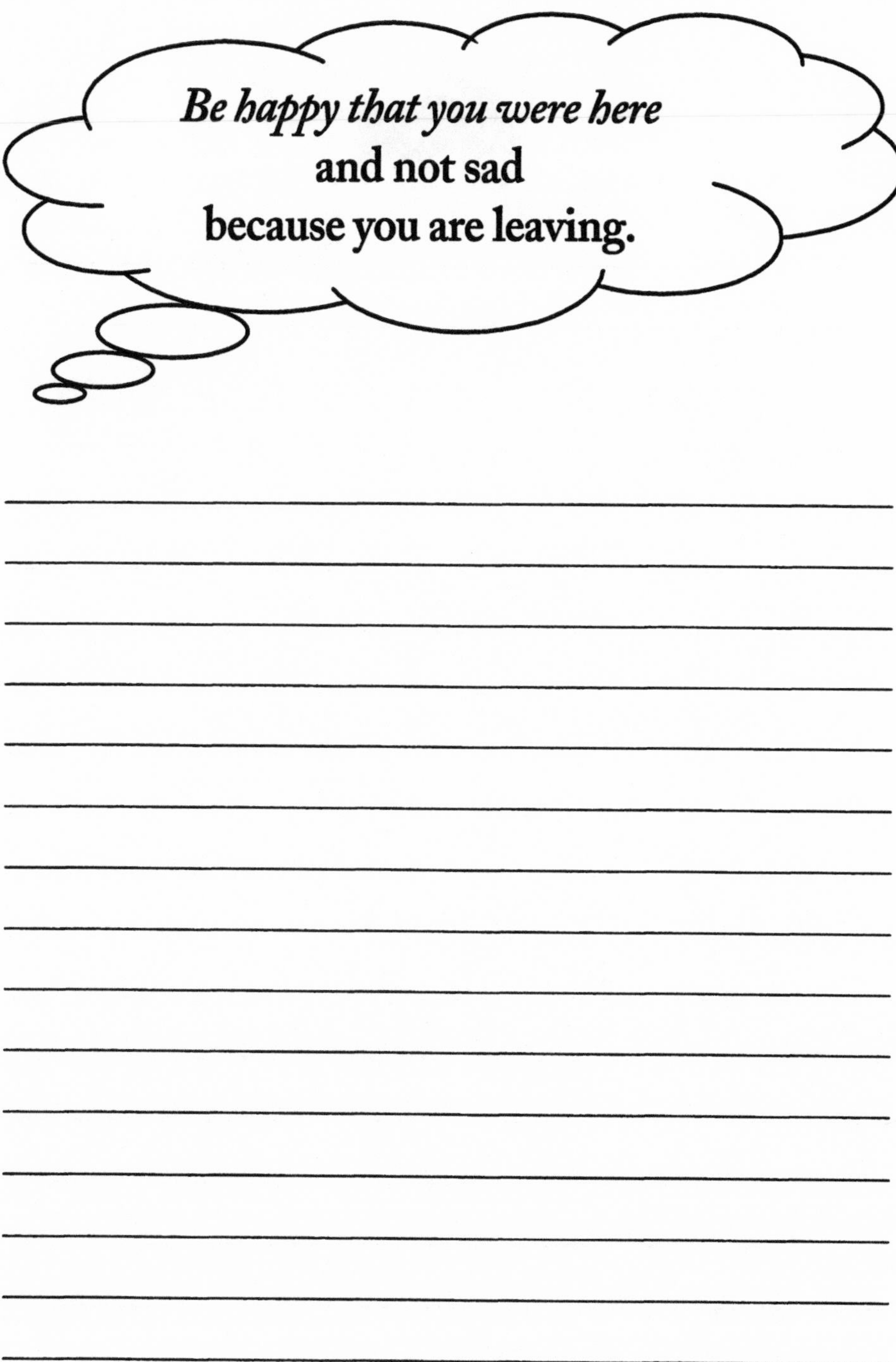
Be happy that you were here
and not sad
because you are leaving.

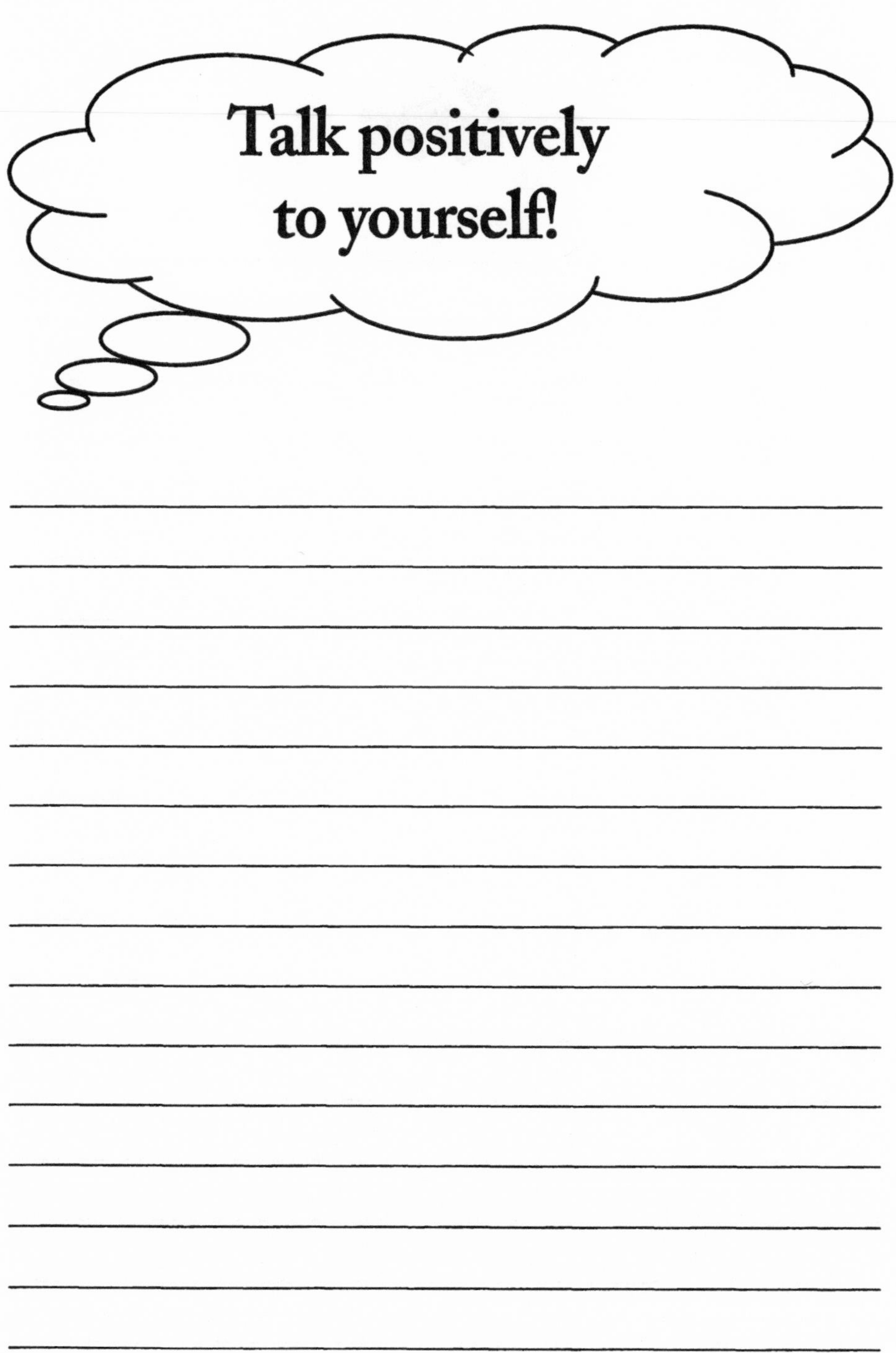
Talk positively
to yourself!

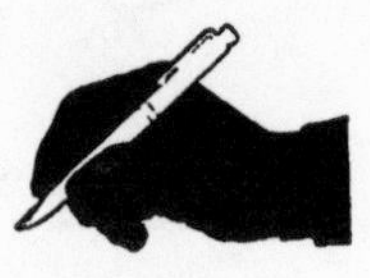

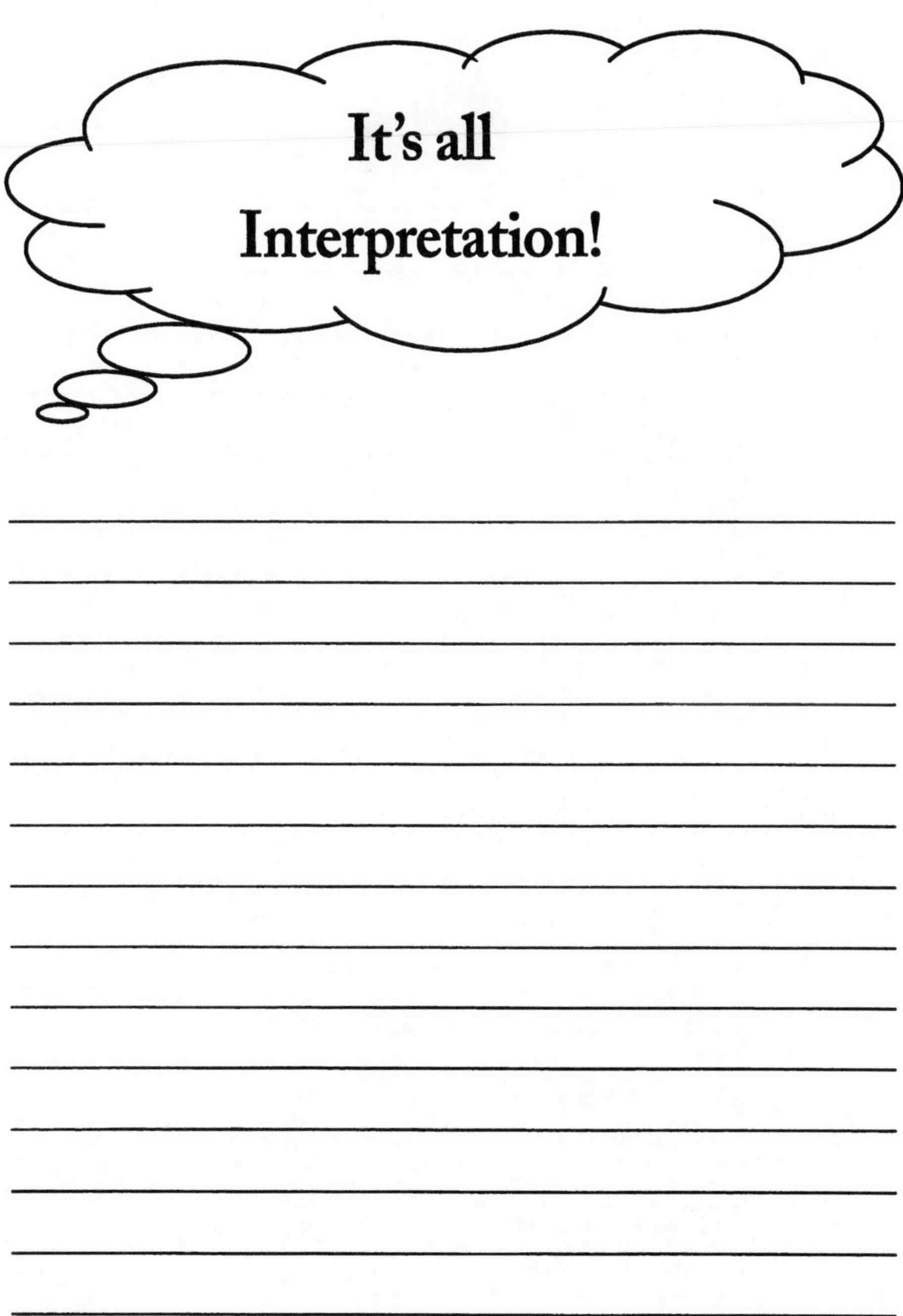
It's all
Interpretation!

To learn more about this quote - refer to pages 16, 17

Goals should be Emotional
and Personal *to you.*

To learn more about this quote - refer to page 12

Death

Is a beginning.
It is a way of winning.

Put on your hat.
Take out your loved one's bat

And play the game they won.
Rewind
Replay…

It never goes away!
The game was won.

You are one.
It's not done.

Change occurs in a MOMENT!

To learn more about this quote - refer to page 18

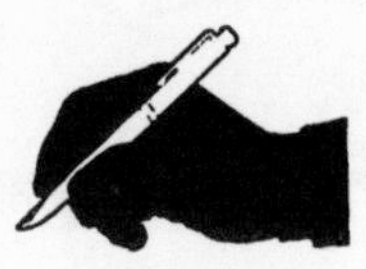

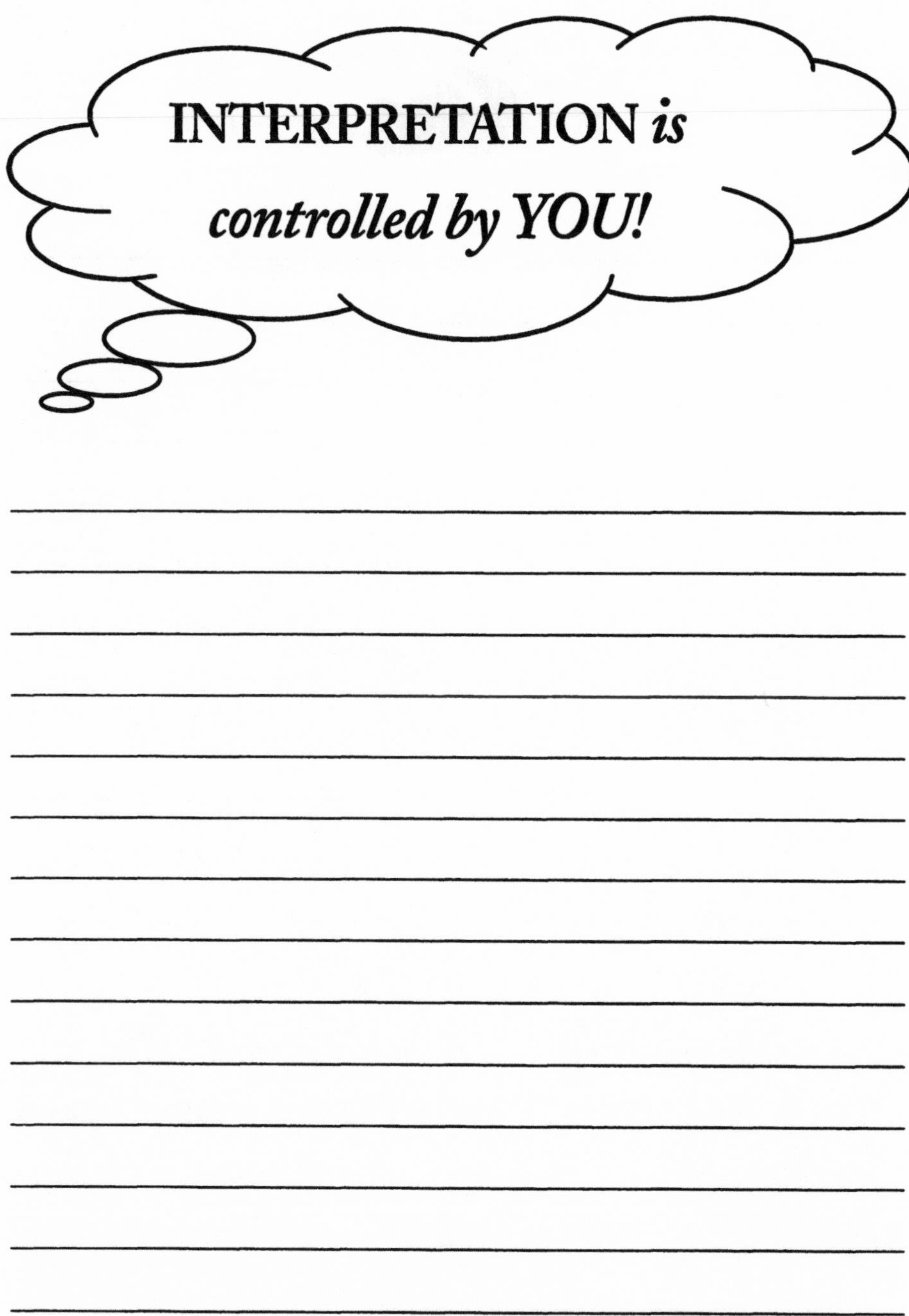
INTERPRETATION *is*
controlled by YOU!

To learn more about this quote - refer to pages 16, 17

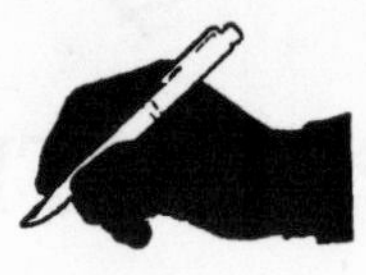

Thoughts INFLUENCE
how you feel!

To learn more about this quote - refer to page 15

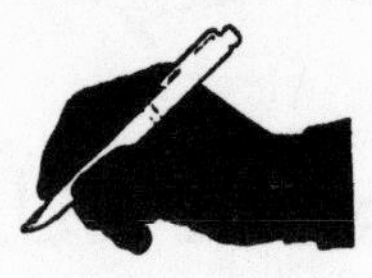

To learn more about this quote - refer to page 19

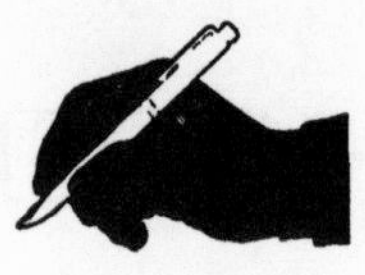

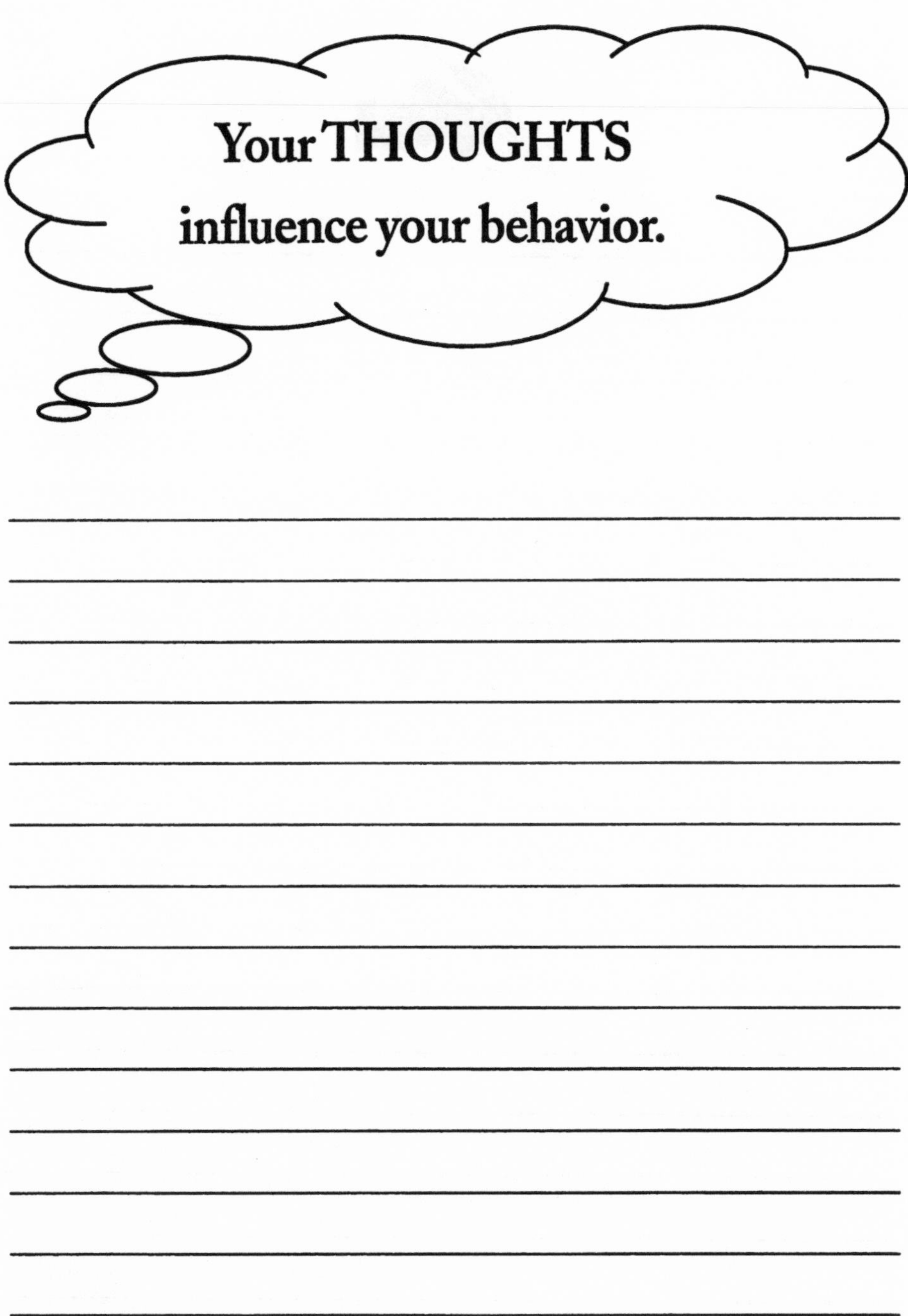
Your THOUGHTS
influence your behavior.

To learn more about this quote - refer to page 15

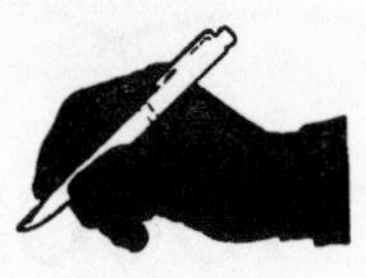

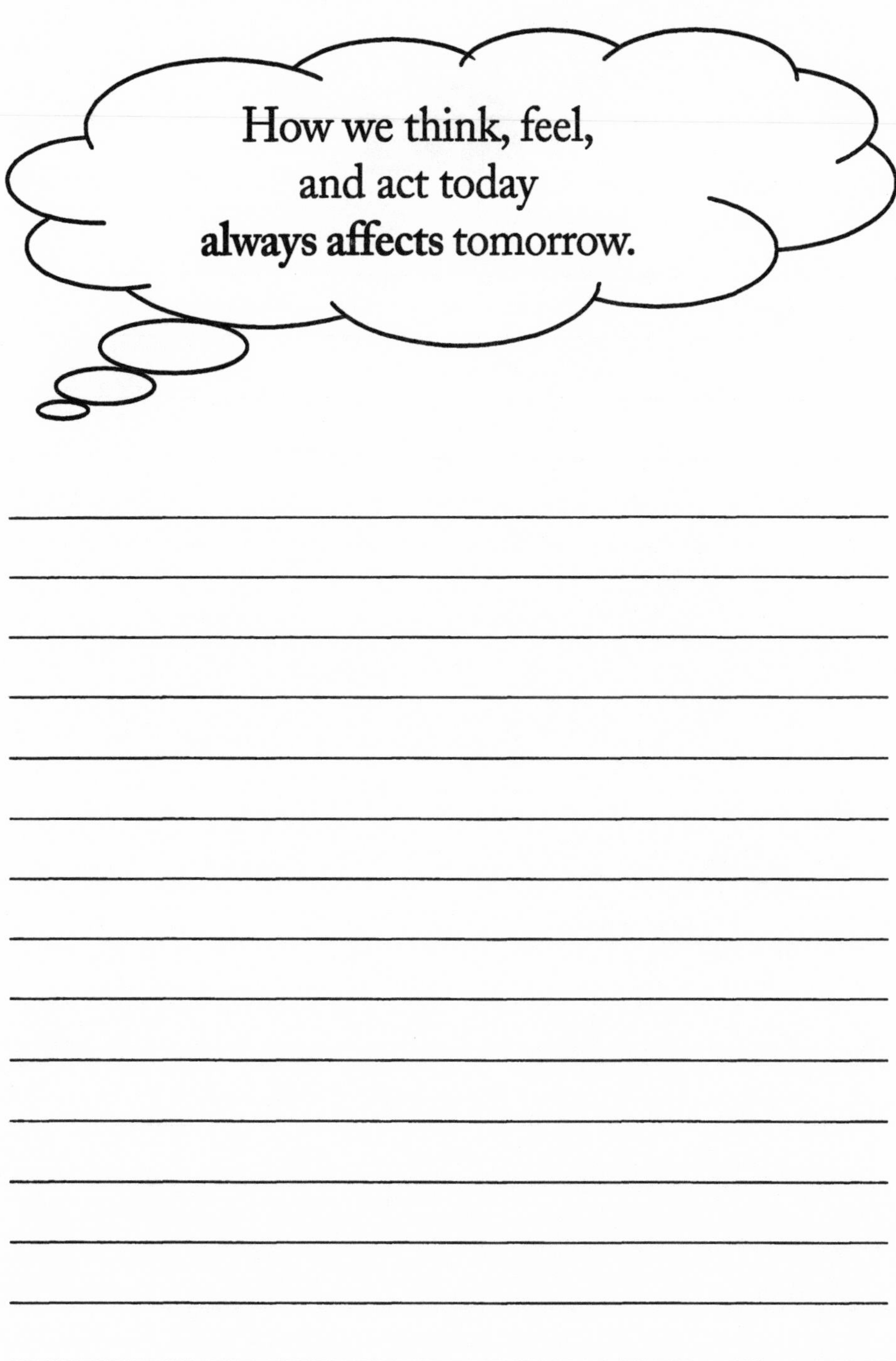
How we think, feel,
and act today
always affects tomorrow.

The most precious
things in life
are never purchased.

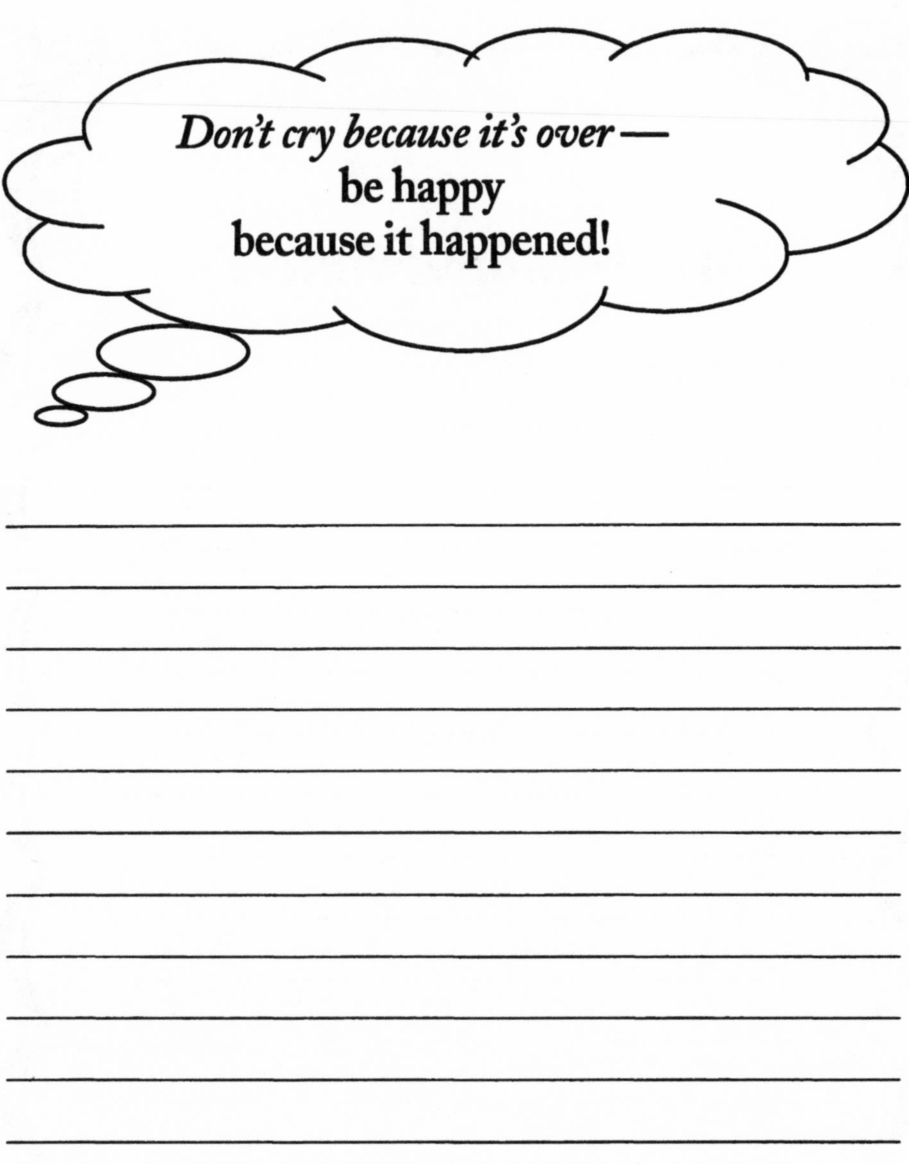

Don't cry because it's over —
be happy
because it happened!

We hope you have enjoyed your "JOURNEY" thus far!

To continue your journey,
turn to page 217 for details
on how you can order additional journals
for yourself and others.

Thank you!
John & Joe

My Accomplishments:

My Accomplishments:

My Accomplishments:

About Pelizza & Associates

Motivational speaking services of John J. Pelizza, Ph.D. and Joseph G. Pelizza, P.T. are available for all your needs.

John specializes in the areas of motivation, wellness, change process, stress management and team building.

Joseph designs seminars to teach and motivate people that how they think impacts positively or negatively on their health and energy levels.

Pelizza & Associates provides people with positive growth materials that give you ***Hope, Peace, Energy and Balance.***

Available Products:

Books:

Newsletter and positive cards

A Journal to Live By
The Big Secret
There's Magic in Discovery
Foot in the Door
Thoughts to Make you THINK and FEEL BETTER

Audio Tapes:

"21 Ways to Get UP and GO!"
"Keys to High Energy Living"
"Staying Motivated During Change"

Contact:
Pelizza & Associates
PO Box 225
North Chatham, NY 12132

Phone & Fax: 518-766-4849
http://www.pelizza.com
john@pelizza.com

About the Authors

Nationally known, John J. Pelizza, Ph.D., is a leading authority on wellness, change process, stress management, team building and personal growth. He is a dynamic motivational speaker to thousands of professional and civic groups throughout North America. John is also a professor of Health Education at The Sage Colleges, Troy, NY.

John is the author of several books, tapes, a quarterly newsletter and is President of Pelizza & Associates, a business which specializes in providing people with positive growth materials.

Two Generations

Joseph G. Pelizza, P.T., is a graduate of Daemen College, Amherst, NY in Physical Therapy. Joe is a licensed physical therapist practicing outpatient orthopedic care. Joe's work with patients in physical therapy has taught him that how you think can impact positively or negatively on your wellness and energy levels.

As an associate of Pelizza & Associates, Joe conducts presentations on managing and preventing lower back pain, as well as increasing personal energy levels through exercise.

Notes

Notes